The Theory of Evolution: A History of Controversy

Professor Edward J. Larson

THE TEACHING COMPANY ®

PUBLISHED BY:

THE TEACHING COMPANY
4151 Lafayette Center Drive, Suite 100
Chantilly, Virginia 20151-1232
1-800-TEACH-12
Fax—703-378-3819
www.teach12.com

ISBN 1-56585-815-8

Edward J. Larson, Ph.D.

Richard B. Russell Professor of History and Professor of Law,
University of Georgia

Born in central Ohio, Edward J. Larson attended Mansfield, Ohio, public schools. He earned a B.A. from Williams College, a law degree from Harvard, and an M.A. and Ph.D. in the history of science from the University of Wisconsin—Madison. He currently holds a joint appointment in the history department and law school at the University of Georgia, where he teaches the history of science to undergraduates, and health, science, and technology law to law students. Before accepting a teaching position at Georgia in 1987, he served as Associate Counsel for the U.S. House of Representatives Committee on Education and Labor and as an attorney with a major Seattle law firm.

The author of four books and more than 50 published articles, Larson writes mostly about issues of science, medicine, and law from a historical perspective. His books are *Evolution's Workshop: God and Science in the Galapagos Islands* (2001); *Sex, Race, and Science: Eugenics in the Deep South* (1995); *Trial and Error: The American Controversy Over Creation and Evolution* (1985 and 1989 expanded edition); and *Summer for the Gods: The Scopes Trial and America's Continuing Debate Over Science and Religion* (1997), for which he received the 1998 Pulitzer Prize in History. His articles have appeared in such varied journals as *Nature, Scientific American, The Atlantic Monthly, The Nation, Oxford American, Wall Street Journal, Virginia Law Review, Journal of the History of Medicine*, and *British Journal for the History of Science*. He is the co-author or co-editor of four additional books. The Fulbright Program named Larson to the John Adams Chair in American Studies for 2001 and he received the 2000 George Sarton Award for science history from the American Association for the Advancement of Science.

The recipient of multiple teaching awards from the University of Georgia, Larson lectures and speaks on history, law, and bio-science for academic, professional, and public audiences. He has given endowed or funded lectures at dozens of colleges and universities and presented scores of legal and medical education talks to professional legal, judicial, and medical groups throughout America. He is interviewed frequently for broadcast and print media, including multiple appearances on major programs for PBS, the History Channel, Court TV, CNN, and C-SPAN. He has also taught in Austria, China, France, New Zealand, and the Netherlands.

Larson is married to a pediatrician, Lucy Larson. They have two children, Sarah and Luke. Together, they enjoy traveling, hiking, bicycling, and working on their 180-year-old house in Athens, Georgia.

Table of Contents

The Theory of Evolution:
A History of Controversy

The Theory of Evolution:
A History of Controversy

Scope:

The theory of organic evolution is central to modern thought. A people's view of human origins, and the origins of life itself, shapes their worldview. It influences their values and how they conceive of themselves and others. This was true of various religious accounts of origins, including the biblical account in Genesis that speaks of humans being created in the image of God, and it is true of scientific accounts as well. The secularization of Western society over the past two centuries has coincided with changing views of human and organic origins. Fitfully at first, but increasingly dogmatically over the past 75 years, an evolutionary account of origins has taken hold in Western science. This view is utterly materialistic. It is perceived by many of its supporters and opponents as hostile to spiritual belief. Some theists have objected to the new view and continue to oppose its acceptance. The public remains divided. This course chronicles the history of this epic development in Western thought.

The first four lectures carry the story through Charles Darwin, who remains the single scientist most associated with launching the modern theory of evolution. Lecture One explores how mainstream Western scientists conceived of origins before 1858, when Darwin announced his theory of evolution by natural selection. This pre-Darwinian view had already moved sharply away from biblical literalism. Indeed, as Lecture Two points out, evolution was already in the air by 1858. Darwin's work built on a firm foundation of evolutionary developments in Western geological, biological, and social scientific thought. Lectures Three and Four deal directly with Darwin and his theory of evolution. They tell his biography and trace his intellectual development as he grapples with the most revolutionary scientific idea of his time.

The second group of four lectures continues the history of evolutionary science from Darwin's initial work through the rise of the modern neo-Darwinian synthesis. This critical period, extending roughly from 1875 to 1925, was marked by intense scientific controversy as biologists struggled to come to terms with the theory of evolution and determine how the process operated. Lecture Five discusses the various mechanisms proposed during the late 19th century for how evolution worked and explores why Darwinism fell from favor even as evolutionism gained support. The next two lectures look at two particular scientific developments central to the turn-of-the-century debate over evolution. First, Lecture Six traces the search for fossil evidence of human and animal evolution. Second, Lecture Seven introduces the decisive role played by the discovery of Mendelian genetics in resolving the scientific debate about how evolution works. Even as scientists wrestled with the theory of evolution, their increasingly materialistic thinking on the subject had a profound impact on late 19th- and early 20th-century social scientific thought. To complete the examination of early evolutionism, Lecture Eight discusses the initial stages of this impact in the rise of social Darwinism and eugenics.

The final four lectures carry the debate over creation and evolution to the present, with particular emphasis on developments in the United States. As Darwin's purely materialistic, highly secular theory of evolution gained ascendancy in science during the mid-20th century, it engendered increased resistance from conservative Christians. Lecture Nine examines America's first popular crusade against evolutionary teaching, which arose during the 1920s and culminated in the famous trial of John Scopes for teaching evolution in Tennessee public schools. Lecture Ten describes the coming together, during the period from 1920 to 1950, of the modern scientific theory of evolution, the so-called neo-Darwinian synthesis. This synthesis applies a refined understanding of genetics to the problem of changes in gene frequencies in wild populations to construct a model sufficient to account for evolutionary change through a Darwinian process of chance variations and competition. Under the new view, a purely material substance, the gene, lies at the heart of evolution. There is no place for God in the modern synthesis, though it does not necessarily preclude divine action in other areas. The result was an increased disconnection between religious and scientific thinking about origins. As discussed in Lecture 11, many conservative Christians hardened their own views on origins by relying on hyper-literal readings of the Genesis account. Some of them demanded that scientific evidence of a creation event, so-called "scientific creationism," get a hearing in public education. During the 1980s, these demands led to the adoption of state laws and school-board policies according balanced treatment for creation and evolution in public school science classes.

In America at least, the public controversy over organic origins continues today. The last lecture in this course examines recent developments in this ongoing controversy, as evolutionists refine how evolution works against a backdrop of continued popular resistance to materialistic Darwinism.

Lecture One
Before Darwin

Scope:

People have speculated about the origins of species ever since they noticed that, in nature, likes breed with likes and produce more of the same. If so, some asked, where did the first members of each species come from? The Bible says that God created Adam and Eve to start the human species and suggests that God specially created all the various kinds of plants and animals. Some early Greek natural philosophers proposed the idea of organic evolution but never fully developed it.

By 1800, the ancient accounts of origins no longer satisfied many scientifically sophisticated Europeans. French naturalist Georges Cuvier maintained that species were not created recently in some singular Garden of Eden. His study of the fossil record indicated that various species had appeared and disappeared over vast eons of geologic history. He did not find evidence of lineal descent linking species, however. Rather, he concluded that the earth's history was punctuated into epochs by life-destroying catastrophes, with a distinctive array of species populating each epoch. This was the leading scientific theory of origins during Darwin's youth.

Outline

I. People think, and in so doing, they have always wondered about how the universe and things in it originated, particularly themselves.

   A. The earliest stories, myths, and writings contain accounts of gods creating the world, the heavens, people, animals, and plants.

   B. The account set forth in Genesis carries particular importance to Jews, Christians, and Moslems because they accept that account as gospel—the revealed word of God.

   1. The first chapter of Genesis tells of God creating the heavens and the earth, then plants and animals, then "man in His own image"—all in six days.

   2. Significantly, each type of plant and animal was said to reproduce according to its own kind. Read literally, this precluded evolution.

3. The Bible does not state when this creation occurred, but most early Christians probably assumed that it was not too long ago. In the 1600s, Anglican bishop James Ussher used biblical evidence to fix the year of creation as 4004 B.C.

C. Science began with the ancient Greeks.
1. Although many Greeks retained religious theories about nature founded on revelation, some Greek philosophers proposed materialistic ones founded on reason.
2. Biological origins posed problems for Greeks intent on devising purely materialistic explanations for natural phenomena. Creation implied a creator; to deny a creator, Anaximander and the atomists proposed crude theories of evolution.
3. Based on his close study of animals, Aristotle concluded that the species are fixed. Rejecting both creation and evolution, he saw species as eternal.
4. Integrating Genesis with Aristotle, pre-modern Christian natural philosophers typically viewed each species as created by God in the beginning; thereafter, those species remained fixed for all time in a perfect (albeit fallen) creation.

II. Notions of evolution, or creation by natural law, revived during the Enlightenment.

A. As religious authority broke down during the 1700s, particularly in France, natural philosophers again struggled to devise purely materialistic explanations for life.
1. Seeking to push back God to the beginning, the deist Buffon proposed that the solar system was created by a comet hitting the sun and that the current array of species devolved from a few ancestral types.
2. Committed materialists, such as Denis Diderot and Baron d'Holbach, proposed that all living forms developed by chance mutations from spontaneously generated organisms.
3. Proposing the nebular hypothesis for the origin of solar systems, Pierre Laplace famously quipped, "I have no need for God in my hypothesis."

B. Except for William Herschel's discovery of stellar nebula and Abraham Trembley's detection of regeneration by polyps, 18th-century scientists found little empirical evidence to support these materialistic speculations.

III. French naturalist Georges Cuvier founded modern biology on empirical research during the early 1800s.

    A. Focusing on the internal structure of various species rather than external characteristics, Cuvier concluded that there were only a few basic types of animal organization, with the various species representing variations on these types.

        1. Bodily interactions within each species are so delicate that any significant change in them would render the individual incapable of survival.

        2. Experience shows that species breed true to type with only superficial variations.

        3. The origin of new species through evolution was, therefore, impossible.

    B. As chief of the French Museum of Natural History during the Napoleonic era, Cuvier oversaw the first comprehensive collections of fossils and biological specimens.

        1. He found no significant changes in living organisms over time either in the fossil record or during recorded history. These types worked, he maintained, and could not change.

        2. He established that certain fossils (such as those of a woolly mammoth from Russia and mastodon from America) represented extinct species. He concluded that environmental changes must have rendered them incapable of survival.

        3. He found sharp breaks in the fossil record corresponding to epochs of geologic history, with each succeeding layer of rock strata containing a distinctive array of fossil types. To Cuvier, this suggested catastrophic extinctions—probably by floods.

        4. When his followers could not find any source for repopulating regions following these catastrophes, they concluded that God or a vital force in nature had re-created life modeled on viable basic types.

5. Fully developed in the mid-1800s, this theory held that the earth underwent a series of floods or ice ages shaping geologic features, followed by new creations of life in each age.

C. While elongating the biblical chronology of creation, Cuvier's theory allowed Christians to reconcile the fossil record with the Genesis account by equating the days of creation with geological ages, with God recreating life after each catastrophe. The intelligent design of each species proved God's existence and goodness.

Supplementary Reading:

Bowler, *Evolution*, chs. 1–3.

Greene, *Death of Adam*, chs. 2, 4, and 8.

Lloyd, *Early Greek Science*, chs. 1–2 and 8.

Questions to Consider:

1. Does philosophical materialism and religious atheism necessarily lead to belief in organic evolution? Is the reverse true?

2. Why would educated 19th-century Christians be willing to embrace Cuvier's theory of geologic and biologic history despite its implicit rejection of the traditional view that God created the universe and all species in six literal days within the past 10,000 years?

Lecture One—Transcript
Before Darwin

Hello, and welcome to this course in the history of the theory of evolution. When I tell new students that I am a historian of science, they often wonder, "What in the world is a historian of science?" Some historians study the history of wars, some study the history of presidents and administrations, some study the history of music. I study the history of scientific ideas and their impact on society.

This course is about one of the most significant scientific ideas of modern time: the theory of evolution. A people's view of their origins, of the origins of life, of the Universe, profoundly shape their worldview. Over the past 150 years, evolution has become the dominant theory of organic origins for Western intellectuals, and thus fundamentally shapes modern thought.

In later lectures, I will explore the development of the modern theory of organic evolution, and its impact on scientific, social, and religious thought. I will also discuss the controversies that theory has spawned. Let's begin with some deep background into Western thinking on origins. This will sort of set the stage for all that is to follow.

One thing characterizes people, as Descartes told us: people think. As such, they have always wondered about how the Universe and things in it originated—particularly about how they themselves, the human species, originated. As best we can tell, with any peoples, people wonder about these things. The earliest stories, myths, and writings from a variety of civilizations, from a variety of societies, contain accounts of gods creating the world, the heavens, animals, and plants.

The account set forth in the biblical book of Genesis carries particular significance to Jews, Christians, and Moslems, because these groups—people who believe in these religions—accept that particular account as gospel, the revealed word of God. The first chapter of Genesis contains their creation account. It tells of God creating the heavens and the Earth, then plants and animals, and then man in God's image, all in six days. Then, a little later, it includes an account of a worldwide flood associated with Noah—a worldwide flood that killed all living things on the Earth except two or four of each particular kind, salvaged by Noah.

To set the tone, because this was such a significant account in the Western tradition, I am just going to read some passages from Genesis, to see exactly what this account says. Now, there are lots of different biblical translations; I have just chosen one of them. If it doesn't ring exactly like you remember, that is because of the translation I picked, but they're all about the same; I wasn't trying to bias it in any way by the choice of translation. Let's just see how it begins. This is beginning with the first chapter, the first verse of Genesis:

> "In the beginning, God created the heavens and the Earth, and God said, 'Let there be light.' And there was light. And God saw the light was good."

Skipping ahead a little bit:

> "And God said, 'Let the land produce vegetation, seed-bearing plants, and trees on the land that bear fruit with seeds in it, according to their various kinds.' And it was so."

Skipping ahead a little bit more:

> "And God said, 'Let the water teem with living creatures, and let birds fly above the Earth, and across the expanse of the sky.' So God created the great creatures of the sea, and every living and moving thing with which the water teems, according to their own kind. And God saw it, and said it was good. And God said, 'Let the land produce creatures according to their kinds. Livestock, creatures that move across the ground, and wild animals, each according to its kind.' And so it was. Then God said, 'Let us make man in our own image.'"

This is the biblical account, the Genesis account. Note one significant point that we are going to have to follow through this entire course. Note that it says expressly that each type of animal, and each type of plant, was said to reproduce according to its own kind. Read literally, this precluded evolution of one kind into another, because each bred true, as created by God, according to its own kind.

The Bible does not state when this creation occurred, but most early Christians, the best we can tell, probably assumed that this did not occur too long ago. In the 1600s, the Anglican bishop James Ussher used biblical evidence—that is, evidence within the Bible itself, to fix the year of creation at 4004 B.C. This was the established biblical view, that continues to the present, of course, but around the time when evolution came.

Over the past 2,000 years, this creationist account—this account from Genesis—did not exist alone within the Western tradition. Religious accounts of origin, at least for the past 2,000 years, have competed with scientific accounts of origins. Science began with the ancient Greeks about 600 B.C. We get the first scientific explanations for natural phenomena then. Although many Greeks retained religious theories about nature founded on Revelation or their own mythical stories, some Greek philosophers proposed materialistic explanations for natural phenomena founded on reason.

What do I mean by the term "materialistic" here? We will see it coming back again. What is meant there is explaining natural phenomena without recourse to God or the supernatural; that nature and natural phenomena can be explained as the result of physical matter, hence "materialism," moving in accord with natural law—matter in motion, as it were, with God at most the remote creator of the primordial matter and the laws of motion by which it operates. This was sort of the account, for those of you who read Plato, in Plato's *Timaeus*. You can see this sort of an account, where God created the primordial matter and the laws, and then left it to operate.

Biological origins posed a particular puzzle for Greeks intent upon devising purely materialistic explanations for natural phenomena. I mean, it was one thing to suggest, as Plato did in the *Timaeus*, that the cosmos was created. Sure, this primordial matter was set in motion, swished by God, so that it would form different solar systems, or suns, things like that. Whether or not it's plausible, it isn't as tough as thinking that such pure matter, operating according to natural laws, could produce complex biological organisms. Biological organisms—people especially, but also plants and animals—seem so much more intricate, fixed, and "created," or intelligently designed, than just the solar system, or just rocks or mountains do. They seem "created," and creation implies a creator.

So, to deny a creator, some Greek natural philosophers—as a philosopher intent on trying to explain natural things is called; early scientists, early natural philosophers—some of the early Greeks such as Anaximander in about 550 B.C., or later, the atomists, a group of atomist philosophers about 400 B.C.—proposed crude theories of evolution. None of them were very detailed, but they had the idea that there was some sort of beginning, some sort of spontaneous generation of life, and somehow species could evolve into other species over time. These theories were not very well worked out.

Aristotle critiqued these ideas. Aristotle himself was not religious; he was an atheist. He lived in the 300s B.C., and was first and foremost a biologist. Aristotle was a very close observer of biological life, particularly of fishes. Based upon his close study of animals, Aristotle defined a species—gave a lasting definition of species—as a breeding group: a group of a particular type of animals or a particular type of plants that breed true to form. They mix with each other and they can produce live young that then can reproduce themselves. He concluded that species were fixed. Rejecting both creation and evolution, Aristotle simply saw the species as eternal; they always existed.

Later natural philosophers who were Christians, in the Roman world and the late Roman world and later the medieval world, tried to integrate Genesis with Aristotle. They typically viewed each species as created by God in the beginning, not just eternal, as Aristotle had said; thereafter using Aristotelian authority to say that these species remained fixed for all time in a perfect, albeit fallen, creation.

This was the dominant view for a millennium in the West, though obviously it began to break down. But didn't really break down until religious authority began breaking down. When religious authority began breaking down during the Enlightenment during the 1700s, notions of evolution began creeping back in; that is, creation by natural law. If a people are intent in pushing out God, or rejecting divine causation, the only real alternative as to where species can come from is either that they could be eternal, as Aristotle said, or they have to come from other species. Where else could they come from? Spontaneous generation, and then, other species. Those ideas began creeping back into the Western tradition during the Enlightenment, in the 1700s.

This happened particularly in France, where the Enlightenment gained the strongest foothold during the 1700s, where natural philosophers again struggled to devise purely materialistic explanations for life. Seeking to push God back to the beginning, the deist Comte de Buffon, a natural philosopher who lived in the 1700s, was very influential in France. He was not an atheist; he was a deist, so God could be at the beginning, the initial creator. Seeking to push God back to the beginning, he proposed a variety of evolutionary ideas in science. He proposed that the solar system, for example, was created not by God, who designed it as Newton proposed, but rather that a comet once hit the sun, and knocked off a bunch of planets—a bunch of "mass," as it were—and they flung out, and they each were caught in a different sort of vortex, swirled around at different layers, and those coalesced into various planets. It was basically a naturalistic explanation for the solar system, without needing God.

He also proposed ideas for the origin of species; that the current tremendous array of species evolved from a few common ancestral types. God might have created those initial types, but the current variety had come from what was really a "devolution," to fit their various environments.

Some of the French Enlightenment natural philosophers were even more atheistical than Buffon. Committed materialists Denis Diderot, for example, and the Baron d' Holbach, both of whom lived in the 1700s, proposed that all living forms developed by random chance mutations from spontaneously generated organisms.

Another very influential French natural philosopher from this period—probably the most influential because his ideas have lasted the longest—was the astronomer Pierre Laplace, who proposed his explanation for the origin of the solar system as a purely materialistic one: that once the solar system was one big, rotating, gas nebula, and as it rotated, centrifugal and centripetal forces would pull in a hard center, which became the sun. As it pulled in, however, it left little blobs of material that coalesced into the various different planets. This was called "the nebular hypothesis." When he described it once to Napoleon, Napoleon asked, "All right, that makes sense. Now, where does God's design fit into it?" Laplace famously quipped back, "I have no need for God in my hypothesis."

All of these ideas that we've gone over were highly speculative, and if you really analyze them, most of them were driven more from philosophy—from philosophical requirements, from pre-existing ideas of deism or atheism—than from empirical scientific research. There were a few discoveries at the time that reinforced these ideas. These were latched upon by the proponents of these ideas. For example, William Herschel, the amazing British astronomer, himself not a deist but a Christian, had a knack for building telescopes. With these telescopes, he could see things in the heavens that nobody else had ever seen before. He discovered new planets, for example, and he also discovered stellar nebula, these kinds of gas spaces that glow in the sky. These were latched upon by Laplace and his followers as empirical evidence to support the nebular hypothesis, and they still stand as that.

Another popular discovery during this time that was latched upon by the people who supported these ideas was made by Abraham Trembley. He detected that polyps, which are a very simple sea creature, could regenerate by cutting them into pieces; they would regenerate the whole. They could be flipped inside out and they would still operate. This raised questions. People would look at them and say, "Look. This is almost like spontaneous generation." It's almost an example of spontaneous generation. If there was one individual created by God, suddenly there were a whole bunch.

These bits of evidence were grasped upon by proponents of these ideas as scientific evidence that supported their materialistic speculations.

Overall, however, the empirical research during this period cut the other way. Overall, even though these ideas were coming up and being speculated about, when people did the scientific research—when people were actually doing experimental work and observational work in nature—most of them opposed the evolutionary ideas that people were coming up with. This created, if anything, a reaction within science against how speculative early ideas had been—a reaction in the next generation, the generation after the Enlightenment, the early 1800s—a reaction the other way, back toward creationism; not the creationism necessarily of the Bible, but a creationism based upon scientific evidence.

No one was more involved in this than the great French naturalist, Georges Cuvier. More than anyone else, he founded modern biology squarely upon empirical research during the early 1800s. He had a very long career in France, from actually the very late 1700s into the middle third of the 1800s. He held important posts in France, was highly regarded worldwide, and was part of the reaction against the French Revolution, against the Enlightenment's atheistical speculation. He rose to prominence during the Napoleonic era and thereafter, and he was an anti-deist.

While these views can clearly be seen in his work, he built his work not on speculation, as the earlier people had seemed to be highly speculative; the Enlightenment was sort of looked down upon by then. The early 1800s were a time when people were hypothesizing out of whole cloth, including some evolutionary type views. "Let's get science back down into empirical research." When Cuvier did so, he found plenty of evidence for creationism.

In his early work, he focused on the internal structure of various species, rather than their external structure. He did careful morphological research on how species are designed and laid out internally, rather than a superficial view of their outside. From this work, Cuvier concluded that there are really only a few basic patterns of animal organization. There are vertebrates, mollusks, articulates, and radiates. The various species that we see out there are simply variations on these basic design types—design types that work. Then, looking at individual species, he saw that bodily interactions within each species are so delicate that any significant change in them would render the individual incapable of survival. For example, the hawk needs its sharp eyes. It needs its talons. If it didn't have the talons that it had, it simply could not survive.

Organisms within, in their internal structure, their organs, are so neatly balanced: the way the heart works, the way the lungs work. The balance is so intricate that if you tamper with anything in an organism, the organism will collapse. They are beautifully designed beings.

He also showed by experience that species breed true to type—that they don't seem to devolve from other types, as Buffon had speculated, or Denis Diderot had speculated. No, they breed true to type, with only superficial varieties, because if there was any fundamental alteration, the whole thing would not work. If there was a major change, the individual could not survive. It could not work. It's too delicately balanced.

From this sort of viewpoint, the origin of new species through evolution was simply impossible. It's no surprise that this view fit with Cuvier's basic Christian convictions. They did fit with them, but in his case, they were fundamentally based on his scientific empirical research, which was of an impeccable quality—an unprecedented quality.

Over time, he became chief of the French Museum of Natural History, during the Napoleonic era. There, Cuvier moved from individual research to overseeing an entire laboratory. There, he oversaw the first comprehensive collections of fossils and biological specimens.

Napoleon was conquering much of the world. He wanted to bring trophies back to Paris, and to the homeland of France, to show his wondrous conquests. At this time, science was a vehicle for showing success, power and authority, and so bringing back fossils, obelisks, and mummies from Egypt when he conquered Egypt, and different things from Russia, and different places that he went, they were trophies to bring back for France. Cuvier was in charge of overseeing the lot of them.

From his research with these fossils that he put together, and from his research with the biological specimens that were brought back, he found that there was no significant change in living organisms over time, either in the fossil record, or in recorded history. That is, the fossils seemed to be unchanged; from the earliest time they were collected to the latest, the species remained the same. This is true of the earliest evidence in regard to anything we had during recorded history. For example, apparently, pharaohs in Egypt used to mummify birds and animals with them, I suppose for use in the afterlife, or something. When Cuvier unwrapped them, he found that the animals, like the ibis, were virtually unchanged, literally the same as modern-day ibis. If no change had occurred in 6,000 years, what evidence is this for evolution? This is evidence for the continuation of species. The fossil record simply stretched this out for even longer periods.

Building on his earlier work with morphology, Cuvier maintained that these basic types worked, and they couldn't be changed. That was why they continued. For the first time in science, he also established that certain fossils, such as the woolly mammoth from Russia, and the mastodon from America, both of which he first identified, represented extinct species—species that no longer existed. Now, this does not directly agree with the general view from the Bible that God created these kinds, and they continued on. This shows his openness to what his science found, and he found that some species were in the past, and some are gone.

Indeed, as he looked more closely, he found sharp breaks in the fossil record, corresponding to epochs in geologic history. With each break in the fossil record, or each period of the fossil record, he found that each contained a distinct array of fossil types—species that are now in the fossils. Based on this research, he was the one who originated the idea of different geological epochs in the past. Before Cuvier, the past was just the same as the present, and species then should be the species now.

He broke it into periods, like the Paleozoic; this is where he found mostly marine invertebrates, perhaps some plants. Then came the Mesozoic era, where giant reptiles existed, breaking it into some subgroups. Then came the Cenozoic, when birds and mammals began appearing. These were different epochs of geologic history. These are the current geological periods that we use today, and he found them in the fossil record based on his expert research, and that of his team at the French Museum of Natural History.

Since each had its own type, and then there seemed to be breaks between them, followed by a new type, this suggested to him that there were great catastrophic extinctions in the past, by some obviously vast environmental catastrophe—he thought probably worldwide floods that wiped out all living things, and then a new population existed after that. Some religious people, though never Cuvier himself, suggested that Noah's flood might have been simply the last of those great catastrophes.

When his followers could not find any source for the repopulation of regions from earlier catastrophes, that is, some land that was above this great flood, they concluded that God, or some vital source in nature, must have re-created life modeled on the few basic viable types after each catastrophe, so that there were new living beings in each type.

Fully developed by the mid-1800s, this theory held that the Earth's geologic history was very old, that there were epochs that were basically different; it also held that the Earth had undergone either a series of massive floods, or ice ages, as later thinkers began to surmise. These had basically shaped geological forces by the power of that catastrophic event, followed by new creations of life within each generation.

While this vastly elongated the biblical chronology of creation, Cuvier's theory allowed Christians to reconcile this new emerging scientific fossil record with the Genesis account of creation, by positing that each of the days of creation mentioned in Genesis, such as, "On the first day, God...," "On the second day, God...," were epochs of geological time, of age. That theory is known as the "day-age" theory, or the "day-age" means of reconciling Genesis with the scientific account.

Then, after each massive catastrophe, God would re-create life. The intelligent design of each species and the ongoing need for their creation after each catastrophe, to these Christians, proved God's continuing existence throughout history, and his goodness, because he created a good world that worked, on working types. Thus, Cuvier's science could be employed to prove Christian theology. This is where biology stood in Darwin's youth. This is the biology that Darwin learned when he went to university at Cambridge.

Lecture Two
Evolution in the Air

Scope:

The idea that species evolve from pre-existing species began gaining currency early in the 19th century. Many factors pointed toward it. First, the emerging fossil record suggested change over time. Today's species did not appear among older fossils, and many ancient types are extinct. Cuvier might explain these observations with successive creations and catastrophes, but to his colleague at the French natural history museum, Lamarck, the evolution of new species from pre-existing species seemed more likely. Lamarck's hypothesis remained a minority view, however, because his explanation for how evolution operated—that acquired characteristics are inherited—lacked credibility.

Beyond the fossil record, developments in geology laid a foundation for evolution theory. Building on the work of James Hutton, the gentleman-scientist Charles Lyell developed the gradualist theory that existing processes acting over time are sufficient to shape the earth's features. This approach posited a very long earth history without catastrophes. The earth's environment would change over time under Lyell's view, suggesting that species living in it must differ as well. This was the springboard for Darwin's thinking about evolution.

Outline

I. The idea of organic evolution was in the air by the early 1800s. Many factors contributed to this development in Western science.

   A. The emerging fossil record played a major role in this development.

   1. Around 1800, British civil engineer William Smith began documenting, for the first time, dramatic differences in the fossils found in each layer of rock strata. Each era of rock formation appeared to have its own unique population of living things.

2. By reconstructing these earlier life forms from their fossil remains, French naturalist Georges Cuvier found systematic development over time: First came invertebrates, then fishes, then reptiles, and last, mammals.

3. During the 1820s and 1830s, British geologist William Buckland and anatomist Richard Owen captured the popular imagination by first describing and naming dinosaurs from the reptilian age. Adam Sedgwick identified trilobites from the earliest eras.

4. By the mid-1800s, most European naturalists (though not Cuvier) and many in the general public interpreted the fossil record as one of progressive development over time, with humans appearing last. The earth was very old.

B. Widespread acceptance of Pierre Simon Laplace's nebular hypothesis established an evolutionary view of cosmic origins as early as the late 1700s.

C. Beginning in the 18th century, French naturalist Comte de Buffon and British physician Erasmus Darwin (Charles Darwin's grandfather) had begun speculating about the possibility of one species evolving (or devolving) from another.

D. Building on the work of late 18th- and early 19th-century thinkers, philosophers G.W.F. Hegel in Germany and Herbert Spencer in England popularized the view of progressive social development (or evolution) over time.

II. In 1802, a French naturalist, the Chevalier de Lamarck, outlined the first comprehensive theory of organic evolution.

A. A strict materialist, Lamarck believed in the ongoing spontaneous generation of simple living organisms through the active invention of a natural life force corresponding to electricity or the nervous fluids.

B. This natural life force or energy continues to act in organisms after they were formed, driving them to develop ever more complex forms.

1. The development process was guided through the use or disuse of organs, which would concentrate the life force toward used organs and away from disused ones.
2. Environmental change resulting from gradual geological change would push the adaptation of an organism in particular directions.
3. The most famous example of supposed Lamarckian evolution was that of giraffes stretching their necks in response to drying conditions of the African savannah.
4. Lamarck posited that these acquired characteristics (such as a stretched neck) would be inheritable, leading to the evolution of new species from old ones over time.

C. The current array of species was not fixed, Lamarck maintained, but rather a snapshot of development over time, with less complex organisms being younger and more complex ones, older.

D. Overshadowed by Cuvier, Lamarck's superior in the French natural history museum, the Lamarckian theory of evolution gained little attention and even less acceptance. Cuvier saw sharp breaks in the fossil record, not gradual development; no evidence of species changing over time; and the impermanence of acquired characteristics.

III. In 1844, British writer Robert Chambers popularized the idea of organic evolution in an anonymously published treatise.

A. Chambers revived the notion of the spontaneous generation of simple life forms.

B. He posited that these different organisms progressed in a series of jumps to the current array of organic species. This development was linear, not branching, and somehow preordained.

C. Chambers offered no material cause of how species change over time, leading British scientists to ridicule the idea. His opponents also stressed the lack of intermediate fossils.

D. The scientific reaction to Chambers's theory drove Charles Darwin, who was already privately at work on his theory of evolution, to tighten and improve his ideas before announcing them.

IV. The acceptance of a uniformitarian view of geologic history provided further critical foundation for the emergence of scientific theories of organic evolution.

  A. Neptunism dominated geological thought during the early 1800s.

  1. As originally proposed by German geologist Abraham Werner in the late 1700s, Neptunism saw rock strata, fossils, and the earth's geological features formed through the gradual retreat of a vast primeval ocean that once covered the earth.

  2. To better account for the fossil record, Cuvier and his followers believed that this process repeated itself, with each catastrophic flood ending a geologic era and laying down characteristic fossils. Some Christians saw Noah's flood as the last flood.

  3. Although Neptunists typically saw the earth as far older than under the traditional biblical chronology, geologic history still had a beginning, a direction, and a probable end. Replace days with eras, and it roughly fit the Genesis account.

  B. In 1795, Scottish naturalist James Hutton published his rival theory of steady-state Vulcanism.

  1. As a deist, Hutton objected to the need for God's active intervention in geologic history. As an empiricist, he objected to hypothesizing past catastrophes to account for current geologic features.

  2. Hutton posited a cyclical process of igneous rock mountains and volcanoes rising from the earth's molten core, then eroding to create inhabitable land. As land built up, bottom layers would push down into the core. The resulting pressure would push up new mountains, and the cycle would continue.

  3. In all of creation, he famously quipped, there was "no vestige of a beginning—no prospect of an end." This would give ample time for organic evolution.

  4. Although popularized in Britain by John Playfair, Hutton's theory attracted little scientific support. Breaks in the fossil record and the supposed sedimentary origin of most rocks discredited his theory of volcanic gradualism.

C. Beginning in the 1830s, the gentleman-naturalist Charles Lyell reworked Hutton's theory into modern uniformitarianism.

  1. Lyell posited that science should only use observable processes to explain nature.

  2. His observations in Italy and other volcanically active and earthquake-prone regions suggested that the earth's inner heat could dramatically shape geologic features.

  3. James Hall's research suggested that the most common rock forms, granite and basalt, are igneous rather than sedimentary.

  4. Intense worldwide fossil research had greatly filled in the fossil record so that the breaks in it were neither so complete nor so dramatic as they had seemed. This weakened the case for catastrophism and strengthened the case for gradualism.

  5. Although the abrupt appearance and disappearance of species in the fossil record convinced Lyell that each species was separately created by God, this now appeared to him as an ongoing localized process rather than a massive worldwide one.

  6. Gradual geological change suggested that organisms would need to adapt to a changing environment. Uniformitarianism gave ample time for these changes to accumulate. The geologic stage was set for the theory of organic evolution.

Essential Reading:

Bowler, *Evolution*, chs. 3–5.

Supplementary Reading:

Edey and Johanson, *Blueprints*, ch. 1.

Greene, *Death of Adam*, chs. 3, 5, and 9.

Larson, *Evolution's Workshop*, chs. 1–2.

Questions to Consider:

1. What role did the discovery of fossil evidence play in shaping 19th-century thought about organic origins and geologic history? What does this suggest about the role of new physical evidence in the development of new scientific theories?

2. How did Lyell's work in geology lay the foundation for Darwin's theory of evolution? What does this suggest about the role of new theoretical insights in the development of new scientific theories?

Lecture Two—Transcript
Evolution in the Air

Welcome back. As we saw in Lecture One, Cuvier's particular ideas of creationism, his particular version of that, dominated early 19th-century scientific thought about biological origins and biological history. However, the idea of organic evolution was already in the air by the early 1800s. Many factors contributed to this development in Western science, and what I thought I would do today with this lecture is to go over some of those foundational developments that led to the emergence of evolutionary thought, which we will then pick up with tomorrow.

Nothing was more important for this development than what scientists were finding out about fossils in the fossil record. Now, we tend to think that fossils have always been around, and I suppose they have been around for a very long time, but people did not notice them a lot. If you aren't really looking for fossils, and you're in the eastern United States, or Western Europe, you do not see a lot of fossils. They just aren't lying around. It is a little different if you're out in the American West, or maybe out in the Gobi Desert, but fossils are not really apparent. So, if you don't have a particular notion of what they might be, they might just look like old bones, and they might not necessarily be a clue to tell you anything.

Beginning around 1800, however, fossils began to have significance for people who studied the life sciences. They came from a variety of different sources. Let me talk about a few of them.

One thing that was happening around 1800 was an increased interest in geological mapping and in geology. Before that time, people basically lived where they lived, and they assumed the soil was about as it was. In the 1700s, there was an increase in industrialization, so that there was more mining going on. With industrialization and urbanization, there were breakthroughs in transportation, such as the digging of canals, and reasonably soon, the cutting of railroad lines, but certainly, already roads. So, they began to look at the soil more closely when they were mining, or when they were digging canals. Also, with scientific farming, they realized that certain places were better for farm produce, and farm production, and that was tied to the soil. With mining, people wanted to find out where minerals were.

Because of this, geological mapping came into vogue; people would make maps of a geological territory, and find out what was there so the people would know. No one did this better than a British civil engineer named William Smith. People had begun to notice that under the soil, there were layers of rock, or rock "strata." Therefore, there might be a layer of sandstone, and below it, another type of sandstone or a type of limestone, and below that, a layer of chalk, with perhaps a vein of coal cutting throughout the layers.

People were beginning to map this sort of strata underlying the Earth's surface. William Smith noticed that each one of these different strata would have a different characteristic array of fossils. The fossils we're talking about here were largely things like seashells of different types, maybe snail shells, different remains of that type. He would notice that in each layer, you could characterize which layer it was, because these layers would spread across the landscape, and only occasionally be exposed. You could tell which layer was by its characteristic mix of fossils, such as how many of a particular type of seashell, what percentage, or whether there would be a particular type of seashell at all. Smith thought that the only logical thing this expressed to him and to others was that of course these different layers must have been laid down at different times in geologic history, that they were a sort of record of the past. In addition, at each age in the past, say, when a particular sandstone or limestone was laid down, there must have been a different array of species living then. There would be a different mix, or some different percentages, of species then, and not at other times.

This began to suggest that there was a rich geologic history to the Earth. Things were not always as they are today. No one grabbed on to this idea more than the great French naturalist Georges Cuvier. We have already talked about him a bit, in our first lecture. He began reconstructing these earlier fossils, not just the simple ones, but even the more complex ones.

He established that over time, there was sort of a direction or order to all of this, that if you went way back to the oldest rock strata, you would tend to find very simple types of organisms—marine invertebrates mostly. Then would come, say, fishes and plants. After that, reptiles, and finally, at the uppermost levels would come the fossil remains of mammals. This excited a lot of interest.

Many more scientists began looking at the fossil record, and some of them found some really remarkable things among these fossils, none more so than British geologist William Buckland and British anatomist Richard Owen, who, during the 1820s and 1830s, first put together dinosaurs. The fossils that make up dinosaurs had been seen before, but they were always in pieces, and it was thought that they were just the bones of big animals. However, Buckland and Owen, who was the founder and great curator of the British Museum of Natural History, put these together into the great giant reptiles we now know as dinosaurs. In fact, they gave them that name. This captured the popular imagination. People loved to come and see these dinosaur remains.

Other important early fossils were discovered by Adam Sedgwick, for example; he discovered trilobites, small marine beings from the earliest eras. It was certainly thought that there probably were not any dinosaurs around anymore; no one had ever seen any. Trilobites were not around; many of these things were not around anymore. Yet, we had the fossils for these. This began to convince a lot of people, both scientists and at the popular level, because there was such widespread popular interest in these fossils—especially the dinosaurs, of course—that the biological history was extremely complex; that it was not just what we have today, projected into the past. Instead, there is a richness to biological history.

Indeed, by the mid-1800s, most European naturalists, and many in the general public, began to interpret the fossil record as one of progressive change over time, with simpler things in the origins, and ever more complex things later, and that the Earth itself was very old.

This sort of thinking about the Earth's history is a necessary prerequisite to thinking about evolution. Therefore, its development was crucial. There were other developments, some of which we've already talked about, that also helped lay the foundation. In the last lecture, we mentioned Pierre Simon Laplace's nebular hypothesis that the solar system could have evolved gradually from a large nebula, which gradually contracted down, making the sun and planets. This was an evolutionary view of cosmic origins that was becoming widely accepted by the early 1800s.

Also beginning in the 1700s, as Laplace did, but increasingly accepted in the 1800s, we begin to see some biologists, or people interested in biological origins, speculating about the possibility that species might have evolved or devolved from earlier types. The French naturalist Comte de Buffon was one such person who attracted such widespread attention. Darwin's own grandfather, curiously, Erasmus Darwin, a physician in England, wrote a sort of evolutionary poem that was widely popular, though not very scientific in its details. These showed "evolution in the air," as were.

In addition, building on the work of some 18th-century thinkers and some early 19th-century thinkers, were two very prominent philosophers, G.W.F. Hegel in Germany, and Herbert Spencer in England. They began popularizing the notion of progressive social development. What we are really talking about is cultural development, cultural evolution over time, the idea that people were much more primitive than they are now; their civilization and interpersonal relations become more complex; that there is a social evolution. Again, this is not the same thing as biological evolution, but it means that people were thinking along those lines.

Indeed, there was probably no clearer example that people were beginning to think along those lines than in 1802, when the first comprehensive theory of organic evolution was announced. We tend to associate evolution and the origins of evolution with Darwin, but he was not even the first one to postulate a complete idea of organic evolution. Certainly, as we talked about yesterday, people had speculated that species evolved from other species, all the way back to the time of the ancient Greeks. All of these ideas were pretty crude, however. At this time, we began to have more subtle and complex theories of cosmic origins with Laplace, and further, more detailed ideas of some sort of evolutionary development with people like Buffon.

It was a French naturalist, however, who first posited a comprehensive theory of evolution, 50 years before Darwin. His full name was Jean Baptiste Pierre Antoine de Monet; few people know him by that because it is such a long handle. He is more commonly known by his title, the Chevalier de Lamarck, or just plain "Lamarck." What he postulated became known in history as "Lamarckian evolution." This was a fully worked out, comprehensive theory of evolution, one that Darwin and other scientists knew about, dating from the very beginning of the 1800s.

Lamarck was a strict materialist. His theory, we'll see, is quite different from Darwinism, but important historically in that development toward Darwinism. He believed in the ongoing spontaneous generation of very simple organisms; that God did not create organisms; no, life forces in nature—forces that he connected to electricity, electrical forces—could spontaneously transform inorganic matter into very, very simple living organisms, the simplest type of organisms, even those below slugs. Think of slugs being brought to life from inorganic mechanisms, because that's what Lamarck would think about.

This fit with the developments in physics of the day. That was when the first theories of electricity had been developed. Ben Franklin had only come up with his ideas some 50 or so years previously. A comprehensive theory of static electricity works had been developed, and it was only around the turn of the century that theories of current electricity began developing. It was found about this time that electrical force induced nervous reactions, or made our nerves operate, because a jolt in a person could make the nerves bolt up, or make the arms move, simply by a shock. This induced the connection that there is some form of life force in electricity. This life force, in nature, not coming from a god, could spontaneously make inorganic materials into organic.

This is sort of the origin of life, not the origin of a species. Lamarck built from that to come up with his theory of evolution; that is, that this "life force" continues to be around; indeed, we have this life force in us. It is in our nervous system. It is how we operate.

Lamarck's idea was that this life force was flowing around in these simple organisms, and it would tend to concentrate on any aspects of the organism that were being used, and so, cause development in that direction. The development process would operate basically through the use or disuse of parts. What he was trying to explain was how a simple slug-like being could evolve into an animal or plant, all the complexity that we see around us. Well, it is their use and disuse of organs. For example, if there was a light-sensitive area on the organism, that sensitivity would have use. Therefore, this electrical force would go toward that light-sensitive area. Continued use would make it develop further, eventually into an eye. Or if there was a stub on the organism, that life force would go toward that, and would eventually grow toward an arm.

If an owl or eagle uses its eyes for spotting, that would make the eyes stronger, sharper, keener. Talons were important to a hawk, the talons would get more life force, and they would grow. Humans' constant use of their brains would cause them to grow, and become more energetic. Similarly, his theory says, if an organ is not used, that organ gradually gets less life force, and gradually deteriorates and withers away.

Environmental changes could prompt this sort of development, because it would push adaptations in a particular direction which were useful for that organism. Depending upon how the environments were laid out, certain things were useful or not useful, and these primeval organisms evolved in different directions to best suit their environments. I've been talking in generalities, and it gets a little confusing, because Lamarckianism is a little confusing. Let me give an example that sort of captures it all.

Perhaps the most famous example of Lamarckian evolution in action—operating, the one he talked about, and the one people always associate with Lamarckianism—is the giraffe. How did the giraffe get a long neck? He would say that giraffes are similar to a lot of other gazelle-like, deer-like animals. Let's say that the giraffe was in North Africa, in an earlier time. Let's say that the savannah in Africa gradually dried out, so that there was less vegetation for the giraffe to eat. The giraffes would then have to reach up higher in the trees to reach ever higher vegetation. This would make the giraffe stretch its neck to reach those high leaves. That would drive life force into its neck, and would cause this neck to gradually expand.

We see this. We know that if we stretched our necks all the time, our necks would become a little larger, and longer. If we lift weights, our muscles will become stronger. If we use our minds constantly our minds will become stronger. That all seems logical.

The big step for Lamarck was that he maintained that these acquired characteristics, such as the giraffes' stretched necks, or our hard-worked brains, or the owls' eyes, were inheritable; that is, their offspring would also have these characteristics. Because the parent has a longer neck, the offspring will also have a longer neck. Because the parent has a bigger brain, the offspring will also have a bigger brain. Then, it would start from that starting point, a somewhat longer neck or somewhat bigger brain, and, by constant use of that organ such as the brain or the neck, the organ would continue to grow. Over time, these developments could accumulate to the point that they would become entirely different species. Thus, you would have the array of deer-like species: those with great horns, those that ran fast, those with long necks; all sort of similar, but suited to a particular environment, evolved through a Lamarckian mechanism.

He would say that the current array of species we see are not fixed in time; rather, any one time that you see a species, such as the giraffes, monkeys, or people of today, is only a snapshot of that species. All of those different species are evolving and progressing in a linear direction, from simpler forms to more complex forms. The simpler ones that we see today are simply those that were spontaneously created most recently. The more complex ones, like us, come from roots that go further back.

This was a complete theory of evolution, but it did not win a lot of followers at the time. Lamarck was overshadowed by Cuvier. Cuvier was his boss, actually. They both worked at the Museum of Natural History in France. Cuvier was sort of his boss, and Cuvier actually delighted in ridiculing Lamarck's ideas. He would point out the problems with them. He would point out that the fossil record, as he understood it, had sharp breaks—that there were many missing gaps in the fossil record. We don't see these transitional forms over time, and there is no evidence of species changing over their fossil history, or, as long as people have been around, animals have not changed; they are the same now as they were back in Egyptian times. There is not evidence of species changing over time. Finally and most obviously, Cuvier criticized the whole idea of the acquired characteristics being inherited. He would argue that acquired characteristics weren't inherited. If you worked hard to build stronger muscles, your children don't have stronger muscles. Cuvier would point that out.

The result was that Lamarck's ideas survived in philosophy; that is, they appealed to a lot of people as an alternative to divine creation, but they didn't gain a foothold in science. Part of the way that they survived in philosophy was represented by the British writer Robert Chambers. He popularized the idea of organic evolution, pretty much along Lamarckian lines, in 1844, with a book he published. It was widely read in England, and criticized. It was popular among certain philosophers and radical thinkers. However, it gained very little headway in science.

Chambers followed Lamarck generally. He revived the notion of spontaneous generation, of simple life forms developing without God's directive action. He posited that these organisms progressed in a series of jumps over time, producing the current array of organic species. He saw this development as linear; that is, from simple to more complex, not as branching out into a great variety, and he saw as somehow preordained within the organisms.

What Chambers didn't do, because Lamarck's ideas of acquired characteristics in life forces were so ridiculed, was say very much about the material cause of these changes. That became the opening for British scientists to ridicule him. They said, "Well, you talk about the evolution of these different things, but you don't tell us how it happens." His opponents also stressed the lack of intermediate fossils.

This very hostile scientific reaction to Chambers' theory drove Charles Darwin, who was already privately convinced that species had evolved, to work ever harder to tighten his arguments, and improve his logic, before announcing his theory. Yet, the fact that all these ideas were out there: Lamarckianism, Chambers's ideas and other various ideas, shows that the air was already becoming quite thick with evolutionary thinking.

One other development occurred during the early 1800s that laid a foundation for evolutionism. It was probably even more important than the discoveries in the fossil record. That was the acceptance of uniformitarian views of geologic history. This provided the crucial foundation for scientific theories of organic evolution.

To understand uniformitarianism, let's go back a little bit to the ideas that existed before that in geology. In about 1800, beginning in the late 1700s, and certainly in the early 1800s, the dominant view of geologic history was what was known as "Neptunism." Neptunism had originally been proposed by the German geologist Abraham Werner in the late 1700s. Basically, Neptunism posited that all these rock stratas that people had been finding, those layers of rocks that I talked about previously, had been gradually precipitated out of a vast primeval ocean that once covered the entire Earth. As it precipitated down it would lay layers, the characteristic layers of rock that we see. Of course, it would also bring down fossils with it, and that explained why the earlier fossils tended to be marine invertebrates and fish, because everything was covered by water. As the water decreased, eventually mountains were exposed, and life began to develop there. Thus, later layers of fossils would begin to have reptiles and then mammals. This basically fit the evidence.

To better account for the fossil record, Cuvier and his followers believed that this process repeated itself, with catastrophic floods increasing the water levels enormously periodically, and then laying down the characteristic fossils of that new age; that is, over time, there would be new species on the exposed land, then a new flood killing them all off, laying down that fossil layer, and so on. It would go up and back, sort of an oscillation of these periodic catastrophes. Some Christians saw Noah's flood as simply the last of these great floods.

Although Neptunists generally saw the Earth as far older than as represented under traditional biblical chronologies, geological history under these views still had a direction. It had a beginning, it had progress over time, and had a probable end. Replace the days of creation in the Genesis account with years of geological history, and take a pretty good shoehorn, and you can make it roughly fit into the Genesis account. That's what people who tried to reconcile science and religion at that time did.

However, by the early 1800s, an alternative view began to develop, a view that was absolutely essential to the development of evolutionary thought in biology. That was view of steady-state Vulcanism, ultimately known as uniformitarianism.

It began in 1795 with the Scottish naturalist James Hutton. He posited a theory that was meant as an alternative to the Neptunist theory of Abraham Werner and Cuvier. Hutton was a deist, and as a deist, he objected to the need for God's active intervention in geologic history; rather, God created all the matter at the beginning, and natural laws and nature then proceeded.

In addition, as an empiricist, he objected to hypothesizing past catastrophes to account for current geological features such as mountain ranges and canyons. As an empiricist, he wanted to have current forces, existing today, account for what we see today.

Hutton's theory is basically cyclical, so I can begin at any point and finish at any point and it is basically the same idea. Let me quickly summarize. His idea was that the Earth had a molten core. This molten core would periodically push up some lava. Some of it would spew out in volcanoes, which we see, but a lot of it would cool inside mountains, push up mountain ranges, and cool into granite or basalt rock. Then, with the mountain pushed up, there could be rain or water. This would gradually erode the mountains, laying down layers of sedimentary rock like sandstone or limestone, which would then keep accumulating as the mountains pushed down.

As more and more layers were laid down, they would push down toward the center of the Earth, ultimately getting down into the molten core and re-melting. As this pressure of sedimentary rock pushed down, new mountain ranges would be pushed up, and the whole process would continue. "In all of creation," as he has famously quipped, "there was no vestige of a beginning, no prospect of an end." This sort of thinking would give ample time for organic evolution to take place.

Although popularized in Britain among the reading public by John Playfair, Hutton's theory attracted little scientific support. Breaks in the fossil record showed that there were catastrophes, people like Cuvier would argue. There couldn't be this "gradualism" as posited by Hutton's theory. In addition, it was generally believed that almost all rocks were of sedimentary origin; even granite and basalt had been laid down as sedimentary rocks. If that were the case, Hutton's theory broke down.

Beginning in the 1830s, the gentleman-naturalist Charles Lyell began reworking Hutton's theory into a viable theory of geology, basically, a modern uniformitarianism that is still the prevailing theory in geology. Lyell started from a position that was much like Hutton's, in that science should only use observable, ongoing processes to explain nature. We shouldn't imagine and evoke past catastrophes or events like Cuvier and Werner had proposed.

He had also traveled beyond England; he had gone to more volcanic regions of the world. He had been to Italy, where he had seen volcanoes, and Portugal, where there had been major earthquakes. He believed that if the Earth's inner heat, as had been suggested by Hutton, was great enough to produce these sort of earthquakes, it was powerful enough to dramatically shape geological features. Add to that the work of the British geologist and scientist James Hall, who had conducted research on rocks, and concluded that the most common forms of rock, granite and basalt, are of igneous origins, not sedimentary origins, that further reinformed the Earth's inner heat origins for most rocks, not having most rocks come from sedimentary rocks. This was worked into Lyell's theory.

Finally, the intense worldwide fossil research had greatly filled in the fossil record, so that the breaks in the fossil record Cuvier had talked about no longer seemed so distinct, and that some fossils lived throughout and into several epochs of time. That rather undermined the idea of massive catastrophes that killed everything, and pushed the idea of gradualism and change. Although the abrupt appearances and disappearances of fossils and species in the fossil record convinced Lyell that each species was separately created, he did not become an evolutionist himself—at least not before Darwin. He saw this as an ongoing, localized process, rather than a massive worldwide event.

These developments in geology were crucial for setting the stage for the development of biological evolution. Gradual geologic change suggested that organisms would need to adapt to a changing environment, and uniformitarianism gave ample time for these changes to accumulate. The geologic stage was set for the theory of organic evolution.

Lecture Three
Darwin's Inspiration

Scope:

Charles Darwin sailed into the debate over creation and evolution aboard H.M.S. *Beagle*. An indifferent student at Cambridge, Darwin set sail aboard the *Beagle* in 1831 as ship's naturalist and travel companion to the ship's aristocratic captain. Trained in Cuvier's creationist biology, Darwin took Lyell's *Principles of Geology* with him. His observations of geological forces in action on the South American continent converted him to Lyell's view. Once predisposed to gradualism, Darwin was persuaded by observations of birds and tortoises on the Galapagos Islands that existing species evolved from pre-existing ones.

Back home in 1836, Darwin settled into the life of a gentleman-scientist without announcing his radical views on the origin of species. Struggling to devise a suitable explanation for how evolution operated, he struck upon the idea of natural selection. In 1858, after learning that naturalist Alfred Wallace had independently hit on the same idea, Darwin finally announced his theory. He published *On the Origin of Species* a year later.

Outline

I.   Charles Darwin entered the scientific debate over origins inconspicuously.

    A. Born in 1809, Darwin came from the British landed gentry. His maternal grandfather was the wealthy china manufacturer Josiah Wedgewood and his father, a prosperous physician.

        1. On both sides, members of his family were active capitalists at the dawn of the industrial age.

        2. After his mother died when he was nine, Darwin went to a dismal boarding school.

        3. Science became an early outlet and led, in 1825, to Darwin's attendance at medical school at Edinburgh, the traditional center of experimental science in Britain. He could not stomach dissection, surgery, or the sight of blood; he liked only natural history.

4. Darwin transferred to Cambridge University to prepare for a career in the ministry at a time when the Anglican clergy served mostly a social function. He continued to study natural history, which was then viewed as a prop to religion.

5. He excelled in natural history, and his professors recommended him to serve as naturalist aboard the *Beagle* on a five-year British naval survey of the South American coast, with return voyage around the world.

B. Darwin's experience on the *Beagle* changed the course of intellectual history.

1. Darwin took with him Charles Lyell's *Principles of Geology* and was converted to uniformitarianism after seeing a volcano on the Cape Verde Islands and experiencing an earthquake in Chile.

2. Adopting Lyell's evolutionary view of geologic history did not shake his faith in the special creation of organic species. Lyell, too, accepted a form of creationism.

3. Species on the Galapagos Islands changed Darwin's view of origins. He found only a few basic types of plants and animals there, but those few took a wide variety of forms.

4. On his return voyage, Darwin began speculating that those various Galapagos forms must have evolved from a common ancestor. He adopted this view after ornithologists confirmed that various birds in his collection constituted distinct species.

5. Darwin kept his views on evolution a secret. He knew that the idea had been ridiculed by scientists and that he lacked a satisfactory explanation of how it worked.

II. Returning to England in 1836, Darwin assumed the life of a gentleman naturalist, living first in Cambridge and London, then at a country home with his growing family.

A. Having married his wealthy first cousin, Emma Wedgewood, Darwin did not need to work. He devoted himself to natural history, secretly developing his theory of evolution.

B. Darwin gradually gained stature and friends in the British scientific community.

1. He oversaw the identification and study of specimens brought back on the *Beagle*.
2. He published a highly popular narrative of his voyage and numerous scientific articles and books about his findings on it.
3. He became an active member of leading British scientific associations.

C. As his health deteriorated, he spent more time at home consumed by his biological studies. Although this research seemingly dealt with various topics, it all related to his obsession with understanding how evolution worked.

III. Darwin's breakthrough came in 1838 while reading Thomas Malthus's well-known 1798 essay on population.

A. Malthus was a gloomy Anglican cleric who maintained that because the human population far outstripped the food supply, only the fittest can or should survive. His social thinking was popular among rising Whig capitalists of Darwin's class.

B. Applying Malthus's theory to all living things, Darwin struck on a purely materialistic mechanism that he believed capable of driving the evolutionary process: natural selection.

1. Despite the obvious similarity of individuals in a species, all do vary slightly.
2. Assuming overpopulation, only the fittest of these can survive to reproduce.
3. Just as artificial selection propagates varieties in domestic breeding, so this natural selection process should create and maintain variety in the wild.
4. Given enough time and a changing environment, as postulated by uniformitarian geology, selected varieties would gradually deviate into separate species.

C. Darwin composed a first draft of his theory in 1842 and a second in 1844, yet he kept his idea secret from virtually everyone. He published seven books of basic science during the years from 1842 to 1857 but nothing about evolution.

1. Knowing the scientific opposition to earlier theories of evolution, Darwin labored to anticipate and answer every conceivable objection to his theory.

2. Although Darwin was never deeply religious himself, his beloved wife was a pious Christian and he valued the social role of religion. He feared the impact of his theory would undermine religious faith by making humans a product of nature and showing that a cruel process of survival of the fittest (rather than a loving God) formed species.

3. Darwin gradually lost his own faith in God during this period through a combination of his focus on materialist causes in nature and his struggles with the problem of evil.

IV. Darwin was shocked out his self-imposed intellectual exile by the receipt in 1858 of an essay from Alfred Russel Wallace outlining the theory of natural selection.

A. From a poor family in rural England, Wallace had developed a passion for natural history, particularly the study of beetles. He became a paid collector of natural history specimens in the Amazon valley and East Indies.

1. Radical in his political, social, and religious views, Wallace favored a theory of evolution over creation on philosophical grounds.

2. He went to the tropics with the ulterior motive of seeking proof for evolution by looking for evidence that similar species inevitably live near one another.

3. Obsessed with conceiving a sufficient mechanism to drive the evolution process, Wallace realized, during a malarial fever in 1858, that Malthus offered an answer.

4. He immediately wrote up his theory of natural selection in a cogent essay and sent it to Darwin, whom he knew had thought favorably of his early writings on evolution.

5. Darwin showed Wallace's work to Lyell, who was one of the three people who knew of Darwin's work on the same theory, and Lyell arranged that essays by both men on the theory of evolution by natural selection be published jointly in 1858.

B. Driven to get his evidence for evolution by natural selection before scientists and other educated readers as soon as possible, Darwin worked furiously to complete his classic book, *On the Origin of Species*, in 1859. This book revolutionized biological thought.

Essential Reading:

Darwin, *Voyage of the Beagle*, ch. 19.

Larson, *Evolution's Workshop*, ch. 3.

Supplementary Reading:

Browne, *Charles Darwin: Voyaging*.

Bowler, *Evolution*, ch. 6.

Edey and Johanson, *Blueprints*, chs. 2–3.

Raby, *Alfred Russel Wallace*, chs. 1–8.

Wallace, "On the Tendency of Varieties to Depart Indefinitely from the Original Type."

Questions to Consider:

1. What role did Darwin's voyage aboard the *Beagle* play in convincing him that species evolve from pre-existing species?

2. How did Malthus's essay on population lay the foundation for Darwin and Wallace to develop the theory of evolution by natural selection? Is it surprising that two people would discover the same fundamental theory independently and nearly simultaneously?

Lecture Three—Transcript
Darwin's Inspiration

Welcome back. As we've seen, theorizing about evolution did not begin with Darwin, but he made it mainstream. Charles Darwin entered the scientific debate over origins inconspicuously. He was born in 1809, interestingly, on the exact same day that Abraham Lincoln was born: February 12, 1809. Darwin came from the landed gentry of England. His maternal grandfather was the wealthy china manufacturer Josiah Wedgwood, and his father was a very prosperous physician, making most of his money through investments, not through his medical activities. On both sides of his family, indeed, there were active capitalists, and this was the dawn of the industrial age in Britain, where industrial- and factory-based wealth was replacing landed wealth from estates.

After his mother died when he was only nine, Charles Darwin was sent to a rather dismal boarding school that he absolutely hated. His one outlet there became natural history: collecting bugs and beetles, plants. He loved doing that. Since natural history was then a key component of medicine—that is, most of the drugs back then were herbal drugs—and his father was a physician, Darwin was naturally sent off to medical school. He was sent to medical school at Edinburgh, which was then the best medical school in England, in the British Isles, actually in Scotland. It was also the traditional center for experimental science in England. It didn't work, though. He got there, and though he loved natural history, it turned out that he could not stomach dissection, surgery, or the sight of blood; clearly this person was not cut out to be a physician. He only liked the natural history aspects.

So he transferred from Edinburgh to Cambridge University to prepare for a career in the ministry. That didn't mean he was religious. Darwin was never particularly religious at all. Back then, however, the Anglican ministry, Anglican clerics, mostly served a social function in society. Edinburgh had a rural parish, and it was a social function more than it was religious function, as we think of it today. His interest natural history made sense, because back then in protestant countries, especially in Britain, as we will see more in later lectures, natural history was a primary prop toward religion, because the neat creation of world, the neat creation of each organism, the sort of "perfect" creation of how different organisms work, the balance in nature, was seen as a prop for religion, seen as evidence of God, and often used in sermons by Anglican clerics, so Anglican clerics often studied natural history.

He needed some sort of profession. He was from the rising upper classes, but he wasn't part of the nobility. The professions back then were medicine, law, and ministry. Given Darwin's interests, it seemed that the ministry made the most sense. While he was at Cambridge, he excelled in natural history. He had many very good, top professors at Cambridge in the fields of natural history, "natural history" being what we would now call biology, geology, botany, various aspects of studying plants, animals, rocks, nature. All of this generally went under the rubric of natural history, back then.

When he completed his term at Cambridge, his professors recommended him to be the naturalist aboard the British survey ship, *Beagle*. This was a time before graduate instruction. There were no graduate schools in England at this time, or really anywhere in the world. If you wanted to go into natural history, what you typically did was to go on a voyage of exploration, where you would get to see the plants and animals, and natural history of the world. The *Beagle* was about to sail to survey the coast of South America for British commercial interests. It was being sent by the British government, with the possibility that it would sail back to England the long way around, making a circumnavigation of the globe. This idea truly excited Darwin.

It turned out that this expedition would take him five years, studying mostly in South America, but then going on around the world. Darwin's *Beagle* voyage changed the course of intellectual history. This was a signal event in the history of science.

Darwin took with him—and this was crucial—Charles Lyell's *Principles of Geology*, the book we talked about the last lecture. This outlined Lyell's theory of uniformitarianism in geology. This was not yet the dominant view; in fact, Lyell had just published this book recently, before Darwin set sail. His professors were all classic Neptunists, believing the ideas of Werner and Cuvier that we talked about before. Darwin knew that he would have plenty of time to read aboard the boat, and so he took a whole variety of books. Among them was Charles Lyell's *Principles of Geology*, which of course posited that the Earth was very old, gradually changed through ongoing, progressive forces.

His first outing on the *Beagle* voyage were the volcanic Cape Verde Islands. Later, he experienced a massive earthquake in Chile. These events persuaded him that ongoing natural geological forces would be sufficient to create the Earth's features. You didn't need to posit past catastrophes to explain what we see today. Just the ongoing actions of the Earth's internal heat, through volcanoes, through earthquakes, through uplift, could produce what we see. Thus, during his voyage, Darwin became a uniformitarian in his geologic views.

Accepting these evolutionary views of the Earth's geologic history does not necessarily make you believe in organic evolution. You can still believe in the creation of species. Indeed, Lyell accepted a form of creationism, albeit different than the strict biblical one, and different than other theories that species appeared at different times over the past. Therefore, you don't have to believe in organic evolution just because you believe in geologic evolution, but it is tough to believe in organic evolution without first believing in geologic evolution: that the environment gradually changes over time, making it better for different species to exist.

What converted Charles Darwin to being an organic evolutionist, to believing in organic evolution, was his stop at the Galapagos Islands. He had already been through South America and been converted to uniformitarianism in geology. On the Galapagos Islands, he saw things that really captured his attention. On these few islands that are about 500 miles off the South American coast, he saw species that he saw nowhere else. They were totally unique. Why on these few islands would God have created a whole array of species all by themselves? Yet, they were similar to the types found in South America, the nearest mainland; different, but similar.

It seemed like there were different types of these species on the different islands. They are small islands, smaller than the Hawaiian Islands, yet on different ones he would find different finches, different mockingbirds, different tortoises, different iguanas. Why would God create all of these different types of plants and land animals there? Yet they only came from a few basic types. There were lots of different types of finches, and of mockingbirds, but not many other types of land birds. Why only a few types? Besides that, there were just a few basic types, but in a lot of different forms.

On his return voyage, Darwin spent a lot of time thinking about this. He began to speculate that those various Galapagos forms must have evolved from a few common ancestors. A few finches came over, and evolved into a whole bunch of different types of finches on the different islands. A few tortoises, a few mockingbirds. Of course, he had to make sure that these were really distinct, different species on the different islands. If not, they could just have been different varieties, like different types of dogs or cats.

When he got back, however, experts back in England confirmed that these were indeed 13 different types of finches on the Galapagos Islands, each filling a different niche for their environment. He became convinced that they must have evolved. He wrote this up later when he was describing this in his later book. He wrote:

> "When I visited during the voyage of *HMS Beagle* the Galapagos Archipelago, situated in the Pacific Ocean about 500 miles from South America, I found myself surrounded by peculiar species of birds, reptiles, and plants, existing nowhere else in the world. Yet they nearly all bore an American stamp. Still more surprising was the fact that most of the inhabitants of the separate islands in this small Archipelago were specifically different. Though most closely related to each other, I often asked myself how these many peculiar animals and plants had been produced. The simplest answer seemed to be that the inhabitants of the several islands had descended from each other, undergoing modification in the course of their descent, and that all the inhabitants of the Archipelago were descended from those of the nearest land, namely, the Americas, whence colonists would naturally have been derived."

Here was his inspiration, in his own words.

Now, Darwin kept his views on evolution secret. He knew that the idea had been ridiculed by scientists and the general public, and that he lacked a satisfactory explanation of how this had come to be. What mechanisms had produced this evolution?

It was not enough anymore to simply say that species evolved. That was not new. A plausible mechanism for evolving new species, while still retaining the basic types, was necessary; we don't see a constant variety of animals. We don't see just all sorts of birds. We see distinct species. Something had to keep species mostly distinct, and yet allow them to evolve at certain times into new types. What could be that mechanism? That's what Darwin would tackle when he got back to England.

He returned to England in 1836, and he assumed the life of a gentleman naturalist, first living in Cambridge, then in London; then, after he got married, he moved into a country home south of London with his growing family. Having married his wealthy first cousin, Emma Wedgwood, another descendant of Josiah Wedgwood, Darwin did not need to get a job. He did not need to be a local Anglican cleric. He could devote himself to science, and that is what he did.

He worked on various topics in natural history, but secretly, he was constantly working on his great idea, the idea of evolution and how it could work. He gradually gained stature and friends within the British scientific community. Of course, he had wealth, he had connections. He was a good conversationalist. He was a good friend for people, and so people liked him.

He also had some other advantages. He had this enormous collection of plants and animals, which he had collected throughout the world during the voyage of the *Beagle*. He could oversee their distribution to other scientists who needed them for their own research. That made him friends. He also could publish accounts of what he found, and those found a ready audience, so he could produce a whole series of books and articles on his work.

During this period, he became an active member in several major British scientific organizations, such as the zoological society of London, where, again, he became an insider in the world of science. This meant that later, when he would announce his theories of evolution, they weren't coming from an outsider coming in, but rather, one of their own.

As his health gradually deteriorated during this period, he spent more and more time at home, consumed with his biological studies. Although his research seemingly dealt with a tremendous variety of subjects, in that he published whole books on barnacles, coral reefs, and the like, we can look back and see that all of them were related to his obsession with understanding how evolution worked. They all laid a bigger foundation.

Darwin's breakthrough for figuring out how the mechanism of evolution worked came in 1838, while he was reading Thomas Malthus's well-known 1798 essay on population. This was a 40-year-old essay.

Malthus was a gloomy Anglican cleric who maintained that the human population far outstripped the food supply. Think of when he lived. Malthus was an Anglican cleric at the time of industrialization and urbanization in Britain. Before then, people were scattered out in the countryside on the farms. One really didn't see that much of the impact of overpopulation or crowding. Now, people were crowding into London and Birmingham, into the cities, working in factories.

The struggle for survival by humans was obvious. The losers in society were apparent, as were the winners. New wealth was being formed. Vast numbers of people were living in the streets, and dying in the streets. This was when Malthus was thinking and writing. He concluded that, "Sure, humans will keep producing more and more and more people, and there's only so much food." The food supply increases slowly; people increase greatly. Because of this process, only the fittest can survive. He would also argue that only the fittest should survive.

He was rather gloomy about these ideas, as I said, but they were embraced by many of the rising capitalists in Britain—the people of Darwin's class—because it explained why they were triumphing and succeeding, while others were visibly being left behind in the really rather ugly cities of industrializing, urbanizing Britain of the early 1800s.

Therefore, in Darwin's class, Malthus's ideas were well known, and they were justification, in a way, for what was happening.

Applying Malthus's theory to all living things, Darwin struck upon a purely materialistic mechanism capable of driving the evolutionary process: the idea or the theory of natural selection. This idea was Darwin's great discovery—not evolution per se, but the idea of natural selection. This was his great idea, or as some people would later say, this was his dangerous idea.

It's really rather simple. It has four basic steps. Let me quickly outline them. One: Despite the obvious similarities of individuals in a species, in that dogs are dogs, cats are cats, and finches are finches, every individual does vary somewhat. In, for example, a brood of rabbits, there's the runt, and then there are the faster rabbits, and then there are lots of rabbits in between. They all vary a little bit. That's one observation.

Two: Assuming overpopulation—remember that—assuming overpopulation, only the fittest of these should survive. The runt of the rabbit litter will get eaten by the hawk. The fastest one is more likely to survive. The one better able to get food, if it is a hawk with keener eyes, say, or an owl, will more likely get food and survive. The ones with little differences are more likely to survive, and therefore reproduce.

Step three: Just as in artificial selection—which is what is done when farmers pick the best milking cow, and only have the best milking cow breed, and not the ones that are not as good milkers, or only breeding dogs with particular traits—that can produce varieties, and that was well known. If you stop picking the best cows for milking, and just let all the varieties breed, or if you stop making sure that your miniature schnauzer only breeds with another miniature schnauzer, and you just let it run around and breed with any sort of dog, they will all go back some generic type of animal. If you consistently use artificial selection, however, you will be able to propagate varieties.

Thus, Darwin argued, that will also work with natural selection. If natural selection is continually picking and is propagating a particular sort of variety, for instance, the faster rabbits, that one is more likely to survive, breed, and reproduce its kind. Consequently, if you have a consistent selection process, and in this case, natural, not artificial, that could create and maintain varieties.

Finally, step four: Given enough time in a changing environment, which is postulated by uniformitarian geology, and illustrated on the Galapagos Islands, those selected varieties could continue to deviate from their original type so far that they would eventually break off into entirely new species. They would continually deviate, because a changing environment would mean that a different trait would be selected, or be beneficial. That one could then propagate out.

If, on the Galapagos Islands, for example, the environment was different than the one finches came from, they might change to finches better suited to that environment, and therefore become a new type of finch. Finally, if they were brought back to their original type, and had changed so much that they could no longer breed with their original type, they would be a new species—the origin of species without God by purely materialistic forces.

Darwin composed a first draft of his theory in 1842, and a second in 1844. Yet, he kept his ideas secret from virtually everyone. He published seven books on basic science during the years from 1842 to 1857, but not one word directly about evolution.

He did this for two basic reasons. One, he knew the scientific opposition that had arisen to earlier ideas of evolution. He knew what Lamarck had faced, what Chambers had faced; he knew that his own grandfather, Erasmus Darwin, had been ridiculed for his evolutionary ideas. Therefore, he labored to anticipate and answer every conceivable objection to his theory, working them through in his head, obsessing, writing note after note, document after document, filling notebooks on the subject. Those notebooks are still available.

That was one reason he waited. The second reason was that although Darwin was never deeply religious himself, his beloved wife, Emma, was a pious Christian. He knew that these ideas would devastate her, because they would undercut the traditional explanation for God's role in creation and the best evidence there was for God's existence at the time, at least in the Protestant countries that latched on to these ideas of God's ongoing need for creating different species. This was central to their thinking.

In addition, on the religious front, even though he wasn't particularly religious himself, he valued the social role of religion. He knew religion helped satisfy a lot of people, and kept a lot of the working class satisfied with their lives. He thought it would disrupt all of society to challenge religion, and he knew his ideas had the tendency to do that. This helped to convince him to keep his ideas quiet. At one time, privately in a notebook, he chastised himself as the "Devil's disciple, the Devil's chaplain," for what he was writing about.

During these years, Darwin gradually lost what faith in God he did have. Historians could go back to try to figure out why that happened. Part of it was that he was continually working with materialistic explanations for how organisms came into being. Since he was focusing on these materialistic organisms, this "methodological naturalism," as philosophers would describe it, philosophical naturalism gradually followed. He wasn't focusing on God; he was focusing on other causes.

In addition, a primary role in his own life was the problem of evil. How could a good God let the world exist as it did, as Malthus described it? Those two things combined helped him to gradually lose his faith in God during this agonizing process. It didn't make him lose his affection for religion, however, and his interest in the value of religion for maintaining society.

Consequently, Darwin sat on his ideas for years. He was finally shocked out of his self-imposed intellectual exile by his receipt in 1858, of an essay from Alfred Russel Wallace, outlining the entire theory of natural selection. Darwin knew what a lot of people had thought about evolution before, but he thought he had been the only one who had come up with natural selection. He viewed natural selection as his great discovery. Every scientist is interested in priority, and he had spent all of this time coming up with a perfect, grand idea, was going to publish it in a grand book; this would make his idea irrefutable. Now, however, Alfred Russel Wallace had come up with the whole idea.

Now, Wallace was very different than Darwin in many ways. He didn't come from a wealthy family. He was just of the opposite part of British society. He came from a very poor family in rural England, but he was very bright, and had developed a passion for natural history when he was just a kid. It was an outlet for the gloomy life that he lived. It was rather as it had been for Darwin off in that expensive private school. The study of natural history became an outlet for him at that point. For both of them, interestingly, their first love, of all things, was beetles.

Wallace looked for a way out. He was smart, he was able, he was interested. He had a knack for collecting that few people had. Thus, he figured up a way out. He could not afford to just go along on a five-year natural history expedition. He had never been to a university; he had never really been educated. He knew plants and animals, however.

He figured out that he would become a natural history specimen collector. He would go for hire to pick up specimens for museums and scientists. He first went to the Amazon Valley, and then he went over to the East Indies.

Unlike Darwin, who was naturally conservative and a capitalist, Wallace was radical in his political, social, and religious views. This is rather normal of somebody who is able but grows up in a rather repressed society, as Britain was at that time. From the very outset, he believed in the theory of evolution over creation, because that's what radicals did. People who didn't believe in the established religion, people who didn't believe in the established social order, liked creationism, because the world was stagnant, and created in a good way.

He didn't see the world as a good way. He thought the world was unfair. He didn't like religion in the way that it was generally established, because it lorded itself over him. He believed in evolution as the alternative view, as many radicals did. That was rather the basis. The people who were evolutionists before Darwin tended to be the political and social radicals.

Wallace looked for an escape, because he preferred to be in Brazil, or in the East Indies, collecting, but he also went there to try to prove the theory of evolution. He had an idea. It was that if a particular species evolved, the different species should be found nearby the original species. If God created them, two similar finches of different species should be found anywhere. If they had evolved, however, they should be near each other. They should have evolved from a common geography.

He went to the tropic regions, where he knew there would be lots of species, many more species than would be found in a place like England. This was not only to collect and make a living, but to see if they were very nearby each other. Geographic distribution would be his evidence for evolution. He saw that, and kept collecting that.

Like Darwin, however, Wallace was obsessed with finding a sufficient mechanism to drive the evolutionary process. During a malarial fever, when he was in the East Indies in 1858, it suddenly hit him. He remembered Malthus's ideas of survival of the fittest and overpopulation. The whole idea came to him suddenly, unlike Darwin, who struggled for years to get it right. It came to Wallace's prepared mind all at once; of course, he believed in evolution, and had been obsessing about how it could have operated.

He immediately wrote the theory down very rapidly, in an essay. He described his entire theory of natural selection. Then, he sent it off to Darwin. Darwin had spent years developing it; Wallace had spent a few hours.

He sent it to Darwin. Why in the world did he send it to Darwin? Well, where else would he have sent it? He wasn't a known scientist. He knew Darwin was interested in these basic ideas. Darwin had hired him to collect certain things. Therefore, Darwin seemed an open avenue to get this radical idea out, and he thought that Darwin might be open to it. He had no idea that Darwin believed in evolution, or that he had an idea of natural selection of his own.

Darwin got the letter, which contained a complete description of his own theory. He opened it up and he read it: "My theory, written by somebody else."

What was he going to do? He had waited too long, and his priority had been stolen. He went to Charles Lyell, one of the very few people that Darwin had told his theory of evolution to; Darwin had only told his theory of evolution to three people before this. He took the letter to Charles Lyell, showed him Wallace's idea, and Lyell came up with the idea to publish them both. He published one of Darwin's earlier drafts, along with Wallace's theory and his essay, in 1858.

The idea was out. It had been announced. Then, Darwin went immediately to work with great vigor, to pull his whole idea together into a book, with all his defenses. He was able to publish that book the next year, 1859. Its title was *On the Origin of Species*. That book would revolutionize biological thought.

Lecture Four
An Intellectual Revolution

Scope:

On the Origin of Species spawned an ongoing revolution in human thought. In it, Darwin does not "prove" his theory of evolution by natural selection. Rather, he argues that his theory offers a better explanation for the origin of organic species than creationism. In his later book, *The Descent of Man*, Darwin carries this argument on to provide materialistic explanations for the origin of the human species and such supposedly human traits as love and consciousness.

The implications of Darwin's theory provoked immediate controversy. Although accepting his theory did not preclude belief in God, it did dispense with the need to believe in a supernatural creator of species. Further, it undermined natural theology by suggesting that species evolve through random chance and a struggle for survival. As extended in *Descent of Man*, Darwin's thinking dispensed with God as the creator of humans, love, and consciousness. The study of man and nature became an investigation of natural (rather than supernatural) causes.

Outline

I. Darwin wrote his 1859 masterpiece, *On the Origin of Species*, to persuade scientists and educated readers that evolution was a better explanation for the origin of species than creation and that natural selection was a plausible mechanism for driving the process.

    A. Darwin could not offer a traditional "Baconian" scientific proof that evolution had transformed one species into another because he had not observed it happen. Rather, he artfully marshaled overwhelming circumstantial evidence for evolution.

        1. Descent from a common ancestor accounts for the existence of natural groupings or families of similar species; creation does not.

        2. Descent from a common ancestor accounts for the geographic proximity of similar species (Wallace's argument); creation does not.

3. Evolutionary descent accounts for the existence of rudimentary organs; creation does not.

4. Evolutionary descent accounts for progression in the fossil record; creation does not.

5. Descent from a common ancestor more logically accounts for the geographic distribution of species than does creation.

B. Darwin also could not prove that natural selection of random, inborn variations caused evolution, but he argued that it could do so.

1. Artificial selection in agriculture showed the power of selection to maintain a variety.

2. The ability of introduced species to displace native ones both shows the power of selection and discredits the notion of special creation by a beneficent creator.

3. Competition and cruelty in nature support selection over creation.

4. Bright colors for male animals and for flowers support selection over creation.

C. None of Darwin's arguments proved that evolution actually occurred, but together, they were persuasive for readers already inclined toward naturalism over supernaturalism.

II. Darwin's theory dealt a body blow to traditional Western religious thought.

A. Darwin's chronology of, and outline for, the origin of species differed on its face from that set forth in the Genesis account.

1. Early 19th-century theories of geologic history had already forced many educated Christians to accept a metaphorical interpretation of the Genesis account.

2. Cuvier and Lyell had offered new chronologies and outlines for creation without arousing significant religious opposition.

B. Darwin exceeded Cuvier and Lyell in dispensing with the need for a creator to fashion individual species.

1. Although some atheists had appealed to science in their rejection of God, most 18th- and early 19th-century scientists accepted either a theistic or deistic God and posited the need for a creator as prime evidence for God's existence.

2. Although Darwin acknowledged some place for an initial creation, the creator's acts were pushed back in time and out of the realm of science.

C. Darwin's theory undermined natural theology, which had become a mainstay of Protestant Christianity.

1. Natural theology sought objective evidence of God's existence and indications of his character in his creation. This was a key prop to religion in Protestant cultures that had rejected Church authority and elevated individual interpretation of scripture.

2. Without the special creation of species, there was less immediate evidence for God's ongoing interaction with the physical world and, thus, less evidence of His existence.

3. Under Darwin's theory of natural selection, new species evolved through chance variations and a ruthless struggle for survival. If nature reflected its creator, then natural selection challenged His justice and love.

4. In 1874, in a tightly reasoned book, the noted Princeton theologian Charles Hodge spoke for many when he concluded that Darwin's denial of design in nature denies God.

D. Although Darwin consciously avoided the issue of human origins in *Origin of Species*, to the extent that his theory of evolution applied to man, it also threatened deeply entrenched religious and philosophical opinions on human uniqueness and dignity.

III. Scientific, religious, and popular debate swirled over the applicability of evolution to the origin of humans.

A. The central issue concerned the origin of man's mental and moral attributes, not whether his physical body had evolved.

1. Traditional Christianity had ascribed these attributes to a divinely created soul, the existence of which divided humans from other animals.

2. Scientists generally segregated humans from other animals on this basis, from Aristotle's theory of the rational soul found only in humans, through the Cartesian dualism between physical matter and the human and divine soul, to Cuvier's classification of humans and primates into separate orders.

3. To the extent that the human mind, human behavior, and human morality had become topics of academic study, humans were studied on their own terms or through religion.

B. Darwin equivocated on the matter in *Origin of Species* but announced for the materialistic origins of humans from simian ancestors in his 1871 book, *Descent of Man*.

1. Darwin did not believe that humans descended from apes (because they coexist now) but argued that they had a common ancestor.

2. He asserted that the difference between the mental powers of humans and animals was one of degree rather than of kind. To do so, he exaggerated the human-like qualities of animals, such as in intelligence, emotions, and communication.

3. Darwin argued that moral feelings (including love and belief in God and immortality) would have survival value such that they could incrementally increase through natural selection.

4. He appealed to Lamarckian mechanisms to suggest that the force of habit could augment the development of mental and moral attributes in humans.

5. He invoked sexual selection to account for the development of traits in humans (such as monogamy) and in other animals (such as the male peacock's tail) that have no direct survival value.

6. Although more speculative and less influential than *Origin of Species*, *Descent of Man* anticipated developments in the social sciences and evolutionary psychology.

C. Even such loyal supporters as Charles Lyell and Alfred Russel Wallace broke with Darwin over the evolution of man. Both maintained that humans were simply too different from other animals for those differences to have evolved by chance variations.

D. Applying materialistic Darwinism to the origins and nature of human beings carried profound significance for Western thought. It ended the perceived divide between humans and the rest of nature enshrined by biblical religion and Aristotelian science.

Essential Reading:

Darwin, *On the Origin of Species*, ch. 14.

Darwin, *The Descent of Man*, ch. 21.

Supplementary Reading:

Desmond and Moore, *Darwin*.

Bowler, *Evolution*, ch. 7.

Greene, *Death of Adam*, chs. 9–10.

Raby, *Alfred Russel Wallace*, chs. 9–11.

Wallace, "Spiritualism and Human Evolution."

Questions to Consider:

1. How did Darwin succeed in so quickly overcoming scientific opposition to the theory of organic evolution?

2. Why would the evolution of humans from so-called "lower animals" arouse such sustained scientific, religious, and popular opposition even after most scientists and many others accepted the notion of organic evolution generally?

Lecture Four—Transcript
An Intellectual Revolution

Hello, and welcome back. We have been talking about how Darwin came up with his idea, his theory of evolution, and his process of natural selection. Let's examine those ideas and their immediate consequences more closely. That is what I would like to do today.

Remember, Darwin wrote his masterpiece, *On the Origin of Species*, in 1859. He wrote it to persuade scientists and educated readers that evolution was a better explanation for the origin of the species than the alternative; that was creation. He also wrote it to persuade them that natural selection was a plausible mechanism for driving the process. Those were his two goals. Let's look at each of those first.

Darwin could not offer traditional "Baconian" scientific proofs that evolution had transformed one species into another, because he never observed it happen. No one had ever observed it happen. "Baconianism," or traditional science, was called Baconianism because the theory was worked out by a fellow named Francis Bacon several hundred years earlier, and involved observation. You observed things happen before you did experiments, and tested and repeated observations; scientific truth came out of that.

Darwin couldn't do that with evolution, because he had not seen any species evolve, and he couldn't figure out a way to make an experiment that would make it happen. Therefore, what he did in *Origin of Species* to make his case was to artfully marshal overwhelming circumstantial evidence for evolution. If you look through the book, there are lots of different arguments he makes. There are really five primary types of circumstantial evidence that he marshals, five types of arguments.

Let me just outline those quickly. There are others, but these are the primary ones. First, he addresses the question, "What do you see out there?" You have seen natural groupings or families of similar species. Let's take birds, for instance. You don't just see every type of bird imaginable. No, you see various types of hawks, various types of finches, of mockingbirds, of sparrows; similar family groupings. Now, this makes sense if they had all descended, or evolved, from a common ancestor. There is one common type of finch, with a number of different types of finches fitting different environments, or of hawks, or of mockingbirds. This natural grouping of animals does not make any sense under the laws of creation; why would God create similar types of finches? He must delight in diversity, so that there would be all types of birds. That is not a proof, but is a logical argument. His theory better accounts for this observation.

The other arguments are similar. He took Wallace's arguments; the geographic proximity of similar species is one he borrowed from Alfred Russel Wallace. We talked about it in the last lecture. This was Wallace's way to prove evolution; that if you had similar species, and if they had come about by evolution, they should be located near each other. They should have evolved, and they couldn't have gotten too far. Thus, you would find similar types of butterflies in, for instance, the Amazon Valley, or types of finches in Northern Europe. That is indeed where you would find them. That perhaps is not where they are best suited. Finches might do beautifully in some other part of the world, like Australia. We've seen that in America with starlings. If you bring starlings into America, they do beautifully, even though they aren't from America; they are from Europe.

If God had created all these things, why didn't he put them where they belonged? If they had evolved, however, then they should be near each other. His theory gave, just as Wallace had said, a logical reason. It was not proof of evolution versus creation, but it made his theory look good, and creation look rather arbitrary—rather silly, as it were.

Another one he made a great deal of effort about in *Origin of Species* was the issue of rudimentary organs. He tells us that we are not that well designed after all, nor is anything else. Why do we have wisdom teeth? Why do we have appendixes? Tailbones? The tailbone makes sense if we originally had a tail, and then we had gradually evolved and lost our tails; we might still have the rudimentary organs of a tailbone. Why would God create the tailbone? Why would he have made wisdom teeth? He was creating all of those perfect organisms; they really were not all that perfect. They reflected their past. Again, Darwin could logically explain the rudimentary organs; creationism did not.

The fossil record is another area that he made use of. Of course, his opponents made use of the fossil record as well, because there were all these breaks in the fossil record that didn't show an evolutionary tradition. Every opponent of earlier evolutionary theories had stressed the fossil record. To get right back at them, to "take the offense," as Darwin always liked to do, he used the fossil record as evidence to support his own theory. The fossil record showed progression. They had seen these simple organisms, the oldest in the fossil record, the marine invertebrates, progress to more complex organisms, up to humans, and mammals at the end. That shows an evolutionary history. Why didn't God just create everything as complex right at the beginning? Was God learning over time, and getting better in his creations? That is the actual tone that *The Origin of Species* takes. It makes it a tantalizing book, a rather racy book to read.

A fifth area that he made use of was the geographic distribution of species. He used many examples; one was foxes. Foxes are found in Northern Europe. When they were taken down to the Falkland Islands off of Argentina to hunt, they thrived down there. Rabbits were also from Northern Europe. They were taken to Australia, and quickly spread over Australia. Rabbits are ideally suited to be in Australia. If God was so good, why didn't he create rabbits in Australia? Why did he create them in Northern Europe? If they had evolved in Northern Europe, however, and then were taken someplace else, the geographic distribution of animals makes sense. Darwin said in his book, "You can always say God did it that way, but it was not logical that God would do it that way." Of course, being a proper Englishman, he figured that God would be logical.

Those are his types of arguments for evolution. I said that he did two things. He also wanted to show that natural selection was a plausible mechanism—not necessarily the best mechanism, but at least a plausible one, because he needed at least some mechanism that was better than Lamarck's theory, in order to have people buy his theory of evolution. His mechanism was natural selection.

Darwin could not prove that the natural selection of random, inborn variations caused evolution. He could and did, argue, however, that it could do so; not that it did do so, but that it could. What were his evidences and arguments for this? Here, his strongest one was artificial selection. Indeed, that is how he starts his book, and he spends much of his book on artificial selection. Artificial selection is just farmers picking certain cows that are good at producing milk, for example, and continuing to breed them, or cattle that were good at producing beef. Farmers artificially select that particular type. The same is true for breeding dogs and cats; you select certain things you like in a dog or cat, and end up breeding a poodle or Great Dane. The shows the power of selection over time to maintain varieties. If it had been a natural process, and traits continued to be selected the same ways we described in the last lecture, it could maintain varieties. Eventually, pushed further, it could produce species.

The second argument he made for natural selection was the ability of introduced species to displace native ones, such as the rabbits I have talked about that were introduced to Australia and pushed out the native species, as did the foxes in the Falkland Islands. That showed the power of selection. It also neatly discredits the notion of special creation by a beneficent creator. Why would a good God let the natural animals of Australia, the Falkland Islands, or America be pushed out by these immigrants from Europe? That is the way God designed it. If it were an evolutionary process, however, and you suddenly brought in fitter species, ones that could outcompete, they would try them. That fit a natural selection-type model.

The third argument was one in which he made quite a bit about the cruelty and competition that occurs in nature. Previous biologists tended to stress how peaceful nature is, but when you really look at it, as Darwin pointed out, there is a lot of violence in nature. "Dog-eat-dog" occurs in nature, hawks eat mice; this competition is fierce in nature for survival—Malthus would describe it for human life, as we talked about in the last lecture. This occurs in nature, and he stressed competition and cruelty in nature. That supports selection over creation, because why would a good God create that much violence and cruelty in nature? It would, however, be a natural product of evolution.

He had other examples. For example, bright colors in males. Why would God create bright colors in males but not in females? Because if it's a matter of selection, you want the female back taking care of the eggs. You don't want her to be too bright, because she would be a target. In order to attract other females, however, the male would be bright colors. That could be explained by a selection process. It is the same way with flowers. These were the types of examples he brought forth.

None of these arguments proved that evolution actually occurred, nor did they prove that natural selection was a process by which it had occurred. Taken together, however, they were persuasive. As long as the reader was already inclined toward natural explanations rather than supernatural explanations—looking for a way nature could produce something rather than that "God just did it"—these were persuasive.

I like to read for you the very end of *The Origin of Species*. It captures the whole spirit of it. It is a beautifully written book. I recommended it to all of you. Let me just read the very last part. This is how he sums it all up:

> "Thus, from the war of nature, from famine and death, the most exalted objects which we are capable of conceiving, namely, the production of higher animals, directly follows. There is a grandeur in this view of life, with its several powers having been originally breathed into a few forms or into one, and that, while this planet has gone cycling on according to the fixed laws of gravity, from so simple a beginning, endless forms, most beautiful and most wonderful, have been and are being evolved."

This was *The Origin of Species*. A true blockbuster. A beautifully-written argument for evolution by natural selection.

When it was read—and it was read immediately—Darwin was already a well-known scientist and writer by the time it came out. It was read immediately. Right away, people realized that his theory dealt a body blow to traditional Western religious thought.

It does this for a variety of reasons. On a superficial level, we can all see how Darwin's chronology and outline for the origin of the species differed on its face from that set forth in the Genesis account, which we discussed in the first lecture, of God creating each of the different kinds, as the Bible says.

Now, that's a superficial objection. While we hear a lot about it today, you didn't hear that much about it back then, when *The Origin of Species* came out, because earlier 19th-century theories of geological history, as we talked about in the last lecture and the lecture before that, had already forced many educated Christians to accept a metaphorical, symbolic interpretation of the Genesis account. Cuvier and Lyell had offered new chronologies and outlines for creation. They still believed that God created each species—Cuvier all at one time in the massive creation, as we talked about; Lyell periodically, over time. They had outlined these theories that didn't sound just like Genesis, but they aroused almost no religious opposition. Indeed, many religious leaders would cite Cuvier and Lyell to prove a need for an ongoing God.

Darwin exceeded Cuvier and Lyell by dispensing with the need for a creator to fashion individual species. This was a more fundamental objection that this simply didn't follow the literal biblical chronology.

This became a big issue. Certainly, there had been some atheists, who appealed over time to science and its rejection of God. You can go back to the Enlightenment in France in the 1700s and early 1800s, where some people, scientists and philosophers, had not believed in God in the first place, and had posited some sort of evolutionary ideas. For the most part, though, in the early 19th century, most scientists accepted either a theistic or deistic God, meaning an active God, a personal God, or at least an "initial creator" God. They posited the need for a creator to create each individual species, each type of animal, as prime evidence for God's existence.

Although Darwin, in the passage I read, acknowledged some place for an initial creation, he dispensed with the need for God to create all of the species. This pushed God back in time—way back in time. If you push God far back enough in time, he doesn't matter too much to us today, and that bothered religious people.

Beyond that, Darwin totally pushed God out of the realm of science. He said, "Back then, there might have been that first organism, or first couple of organisms created, and then everything evolved. Science is not going to worry about that. We're only going to worry about what has happened since then." Consequently, the theory pushes back in time for everybody, but it totally pushes God out of science. This created theological implications.

There's an even more fundamental objection from a religious viewpoint, in regard to what Darwin was doing. Of course, all of these things were realized immediately. Right away. The first people who read it saw these points, because these points about the atheistic implications of evolution had been debated ever since Buffon, Charles Darwin's grandfather Erasmus, and other people had been speculating about these ideas. Darwin's theory of natural selection undermined natural theology. It was not his theory of evolution, but his explanation of natural selection that did so. Natural theology had become a mainstay of Protestant Christianity. I'll explain that a little bit, since that was such a center for controversy.

Natural theology sought evidence of God's existence, and indications of God's character in God's creation. This had become a key prop to religion in Protestant churches that had rejected papal authority, the Roman Catholic authority, the Church authority, and had elevated individual interpretation of scripture. You have probably all heard Luther's phrase, "The priesthood of all believers." This stresses that everyone should go back to the Bible, "sola scriptura"; the Bible is our one source of truth and each individual inspired by God could read the Bible and come up with their own religious truth.

The Bible says a lot of things, and the Catholic Church did not have that problem, because they had set church authority. In Protestant countries, however, the church had evermore relied on, "You can read the Bible any way you want to, but look at what God created. Look at all of these wonderful plants and animals. Look at the balance in nature. The plants are producing oxygen, and the animals are using it. The species are perfectly designed; the eyes are working, whole bodies are working to create a balanced organism. Change anything, and it doesn't work. That certainly shows that there must be a God who designed these things. He must be a good God, because nature is good. Nature's law works. It produced us; we seem to be happy. The plants seem to work, the animals seem to work. That shows as the nature and character of God."

That had become an increasingly important prop to religion in Protestant Europe, especially in England. Without the special creation of species, there was less immediate evidence of God's ongoing interaction with the physical world, and less evidence of His existence. Nature's fine design was no longer His doing.

Under Darwin's theory of evolution, new species evolved not by any sort of beneficial laws; how did they evolve? They evolved through random chance mutations at birth. How were they selected? Through a ruthless "struggle for survival" process.

If God had designed these laws to produce species, then what was nature saying about its creator? It was saying that the creator used chance and cruelty. This sort of view, natural selection, challenged God's justice and love, if this was his means to create, if these were the laws he used to set about creating new things.

This was really the fundamental challenge of Darwinism for traditional Western religion at the time. Under Darwin's laws, there were random chance and struggle for survival. This challenge is captured in an article he wrote. I want to read a little passage from it. When his book came out, one of his main proponents in America was a fellow named Asa Gray, the great Harvard botanist. Gray was also devoutly religious, as well as a great botanist. He worked out the publication of *Origin of Species* in America. He was one who organized it and wrote the initial favorable reviews. He was troubled, however, by its implications for religion, so he wrote a letter about that to Darwin, and Darwin wrote back with his own views on this, in 1860, shortly after *Origin of Species* was published. He wrote:

> "I had no intention to write atheistically, but I own that I cannot see as plainly as others do, and as I should wish to do, evidence of design and beneficence on all sides of us. There seems to be too much misery in the world. I cannot persuade myself that a beneficent and omnipotent God would have designedly created the Ichneumonidae with the express intent of feeding within the living bodies of caterpillars, or that a cat should play with mice. Not believing this, I see no necessity in the belief that the eye was expressly designed."

This last reference was that often, in evidence of the neat design that God did of organisms, one only had to look at how neatly the eye was balanced, and what a miraculous creation it was. It was a common sermon application. "We know there's a God, because look how neat he makes the eye." Darwin, however, said, "I just can't see it."

In a tightly reasoned 1874 book, noted Princeton theologian Charles Hodge spoke for many when he concluded that Darwin's denial of the design in nature denied God. Darwin knew that the greatest controversy about his book would come from its discussion on humans' evolution. It was one thing to say animals evolved, but to say that people evolved would create the most controversy. He had agonized about this in his notebooks, and he intentionally all but left it out of *The Origin of Species*. He made some allusions to it, but he never specifically dealt with the extent to which his theory applied to humans. More than anything else, this would enrage traditionally religious people, and run against traditional philosophies. Consequently, he downplayed that. That is where the popular debate was, however. There was certainly debate over the techniques of evolution, how it worked, and whether it worked. The scientific, religious, and popular debate swirled over the applicability of evolution for humans.

The central concern was not that our bodies evolved. People were willing to say, "I will accept the evolution of the human body, but how could the human mind evolve? How could human tool-making evolve? How could moral attributes, such as love, evolve?" Those were the real controversies.

Traditional Christianity had attributed these attributes to divinely created souls, in that we all have souls that were created by God, and that the existence of these souls, which only humans have, fundamentally divide humans from other animals. Scientists had generally bought this view. We can go all the way back to Aristotle and his Greek ideas, where, in ancient Greece, Aristotle posited that only humans have actual souls, and that they divide humans, fundamentally, from all different animals.

Descartesian dualism postulated similar things. Humans were fundamentally different from all other animals because only humans have souls. That was the great divide, the great dualism: only the human soul and God on one side, material existence on the other.

Cuvier had pushed this further. He had classified humans in an entirely separate order from primates such as monkeys and orangutans. As such, to the extent that the human mind, human behavior, and human morality had become topics of academic study, humans were studied on their own terms, or through religion.

As I said, Darwin had equivocated on this matter in *Origin of Species*, but he announced his support for, and threw his entire weight behind, origins for humans from simian ancestors in his 1871 book, his other great book, *The Descent of Man*.

Let's look into this, because this was a real controversy. "You can have everything else evolve, but humans evolve?" That's what people really care about. We care about ourselves.

Darwin did not believe that humans descended from apes. He couldn't have believed that, because both of them exist now, so humans could not have descended down from them. Rather, what he argued was that humans and apes had a common ancestor, as did monkeys and other primates.

When he made this argument in *The Descent of Man*, he looked at the two main differences that scientists and people in general thought divided humans from other animals: the mind, in that humans' minds are fundamentally different than animals' minds, and moral behavior, moral attributes are different.

He focused on these two, because there wasn't all that much controversy on whether or not the human body had evolved. It was that the mind had been created by God; it was, "Is the soul different?" The soul comes out in the mind and moral attributes.

It is pretty easy to read *Origin of Species* today, but *The Descent of Man* is pretty tough to read today. He tried to downplay the differences between the human mind and the animal mind. He did this systematically throughout his book by exaggerating the human-like qualities of animals: their intelligence, their emotions, their ability to communicate. It is far above what scientists would accept today. He also downplays the mental attributes of some humans. Consequently, he takes the "lower forms of humans," as he describes the Australian aborigines, for instance, and makes them almost apelike, almost like primates in his description. He has a hierarchy of humans. It was a common viewpoint in the late 1800s.

That was one way he tried to bridge this gap between animals and humans. On moral attributes, he argued that even the highest moral feelings, such as love, belief in God, and belief in immortality could have evolved over time, because they have survival value; that because we love each other, our species is more likely to survive. Because we believe in God and have a sense of purpose, we are more likely to work hard and survive. Therefore, these attributes have survival value, and could have gradually increased through natural selection; they didn't have to be imposed from without by a God.

As he made these arguments, he appealed heavily to Lamarckian mechanisms. It was interesting. Darwin became more of a Lamarckian over time. In later editions of even *Origin of Species*, as certainly is true of *Descent of Man*, you almost think you're reading Lamarck, at times. This is because it's easy to show how some things like love, and moral attributes develop as acquired characteristics. We love our offspring, and so they have more love. Rather than through the "survival of the fittest" or a natural selection process of acquired characteristics, we see more of these ideas worked into his book.

He also invokes sexual selection to account for development of certain traits. You don't see much of sexual selection in *Origin of Species,* but you see a lot of it in *Descent of Man*. That is, you must reproduce something that a mate might choose, such as the peacock's tail. Why would male peacocks have this incredible tail that actually makes it tougher to fly and survive? It is there because the mate likes the peacock's tail, so it attracts mates, and therefore sexual selection explains the peacock's tail, explains monogamy. Why would humans be monogamous, when certainly spreading as much seed as possible would produce more offspring? Because if the mate is selected for that, it could exist. This is a type of explanation.

Now, you're going to say that these are pretty speculative, and they were. It made this book not nearly as credible as *Origin of Species*. *Origin of Species* is pretty solid. If you read that, it is very persuasive. If you read this, you can think of a million explanations as to why it doesn't work. It's filled with "just so" stories that could be, but really seem like idle speculations that somebody came up with. Yet, it was an important book, because it tied the descent of humans to other animals. Darwin spoke on those issues, and it would also anticipate later developments in the social sciences and in evolutionary psychology that we will talk about in later lectures.

Even some of Darwin's most loyal supporters could not buy these arguments. Charles Lyell, and even Alfred Russel Wallace, did not buy human evolution. They thought that the human mind and moral attributes were simply too different from animals; that they could not have evolved in a step-by-step process, and that this, and this alone, must have been breathed into an evolved ape and made humans.

Yet, applying materialistic Darwinism to the origins and nature of human beings carried profound significance for Western thought. It ended the perceived divide between humans and the rest of nature enshrined by biblical religion and Aristotelian science. It created the controversy that we have lived with ever since.

Lecture Five
Debates over Mechanism

Scope:

Buoyed by Darwin's arguments, the idea of evolution gained ascendancy in Western biology. It offered a plausible explanation for the origin of species and raised a host of new issues for scientific study. By 1875, virtually all biologists in Europe and America adopted an evolutionary view of origins.

Even as biologists accepted the basic theory of evolution, they came to doubt the sufficiency of Darwin's idea that the evolutionary process proceeded through random, inborn variations selected by a competitive struggle for survival. Alternative theories flourished, particularly a revived Lamarckism invoking the inheritance of acquired characteristics, vitalist notions that indwelling life forces pushed the development of species, and the belief that God guided evolution. In addition to addressing scientific problems with Darwinism, these alternative theories diminished the social and religious implications of evolutionary thought.

Outline

I.   The theory of organic evolution (i.e., that species descend from prior species) quickly found near universal acceptance among American and European scientists.

  A. The first printing of *Origin of Species* sold out on the first day. It was widely discussed and debated—critically at first, but more favorably over time.

  B. Within a decade after Darwin and Wallace announced their theory of evolution, the idea that species evolved from other species dominated biological thought in the United States and Britain.

  1. Central to this conversion was a conviction that the world is governed by natural law rather than divine caprice, which had been Darwin's principal thrust.

  2. Harvard botanist Asa Gray, a devout Christian and early Darwin confidant, worked to smooth the reception of Darwinism in the United States.

  3. By 1870, only three prominent American naturalists—Louis Agassiz at Harvard, Arnold Guyot at

Princeton, and John Dawson at McGill—still rejected the basic idea that species evolve from other species.

4. Acceptance came somewhat slower in Britain but was essentially complete by 1880. T.H. Huxley wrote to Darwin in 1868: "You will have the rare happiness to see your ideas triumphant during your lifetime."

C. The most prominent holdouts in the scientific community were established proponents of Cuvier's view of successive creation, not believers in biblical creationism.

1. Agassiz in the United States and Richard Owen in Britain argued that complex organs (such as the eye) and interdependent species (such as flowers and bees) simply could not have evolved by intermediate steps. They must have been designed.

2. Opponents also stressed the gaps and missing links in the fossil record, although they readily accepted a long geologic history and the appearance and disappearance of species over time. Indeed, Agassiz had "discovered" the ice ages.

3. These opponents never called themselves "creationists" or referred to their ideas as "creationism." Agassiz was not religious.

4. Darwin acknowledged the force of these objections, and once described the eye as "an antidote to atheism," but maintained that more research would prove him right.

5. These last holdouts simply died out, Dawson being the last of them when he died in 1899, and were never replaced. Their students all became evolutionists.

II. The theory of evolution raised a host of interesting new questions that quickly came to dominate the research agenda of field naturalists and laboratory biologists.

A. The best scientific evidence for evolution came from highly technical studies of morphological relationships among species.

1. Biologists detected ever more rudimentary organs in species—seemingly useless holdovers from their ancestral forms.

2. They also found structural similarities among supposedly related species that had no functional

explanation, such as the hand-like bones of marine mammal flippers.

3. Lunged fish were seen as a link between true fish and land animals.

4. The duck-billed platypus and marsupials were seen as steps toward mammals.

5. Ernst Haeckel postulated the hypothetical *Pithecanthropus* (Greek for "ape-man") as the missing link of humans and apes.

B. Microscopists, particularly in Germany, sought evidence of evolution in the study of animal embryos.

1. Believing in progressive development, Haeckel and his followers postulated that "higher" organisms should exhibit more embryonic development than "lower" ones, with "higher" embryos "recapitulating" past stages of evolution.

2. During the 1870s and 1880s, seeing what they wanted to see in the microscopic world of embryos, Haeckel and others offered highly influential scientific "proof" of evolution in the alleged similarity of embryonic development.

3. Haeckel's views reflected his belief in Lamarckian evolution and were later discredited. Darwinian evolution should not fit the "recapitulation" model.

C. Bio-geographers followed Alfred Russel Wallace in giving an evolutionary interpretation to the geographic distribution of species.

1. The so-called "Wallace line" dividing Asian from Australian species was simply the most distinct of several barriers dividing the earth in biologically distinct regions. Evolution provided a more logical explanation for these divisions than creation did.

2. Naturalists looked for and found an ever-increasing array of intermediate species linking similar types. Just as Wallace had predicted, these similar species typically were found just beyond a barrier to distribution from kindred types.

3. Holdover types, such as giant reptiles, marsupials, and the duck-billed platypus, tended to be found in the most isolated places, such as oceanic islands and Australia.

D. With limited success, paleontologists began filling out the evolutionary tree of life with discoveries from the fossil record. Pointing to these finds, American paleontologist Edward Drinker Cope in 1872 declared evolution an "ascertained fact."

III. Even as the theory of evolution gained acceptance during the 1860s and 1870s, doubts grew as to the sufficiency of natural selection alone to drive the process.

A. Evidence and interpretations mounted against natural selection.

1. As originally conceived by Darwin and Wallace, the natural selection of random variations would lead to evolution, but under the prevailing notions of inheritance, even beneficial variation could not survive in the wild.

2. Estimates from the physical sciences as to the age of the solar system (200 million years) did not give enough time for natural selection alone to produce life as it then existed.

3. Many scientists, including Wallace, denied that the natural selection of random variations could lead to the major jump in intelligence and morality separating humans from other animals.

4. Continued evidence of gaps in the fossil record convinced some scientists that evolution must proceed in spurts and stops that were unexplainable under a theory of natural selection.

5. Even Darwin and Wallace increasingly sought other evolutionary mechanisms to supplement natural selection, though Darwin clung to materialism.

B. Three main alternatives to classical Darwinism emerged.

    1. Neo-Lamarckian evolution relied on the inheritance of acquired characteristics modified through use and disuse to account for the speed and direction of evolutionary development. Darwin increasingly appealed to this approach.

    2. Orthogenesis attributed evolution to internal forces within living things that pushed them to develop in fixed directions.

    3. Theistic evolution saw God as a source and guide of variations along lines beneficial to species.

C. These alternatives potentially fit the scientific evidence for the occurrence of evolution without all the religious and philosophical consequences of natural selection. Theistic evolution and orthogenesis were particularly compatible with a spiritual view.

D. By 1900, natural selection had been so discredited that few scientists accepted it as the mechanism of evolution. By all accounts, however, they all accepted the so-called "fact" that species evolve.

Essential Reading:

Bowler, *Evolution*, chs. 7–9.

Supplementary Reading:

Bowler, *The Non-Darwinian Revolution*.

Larson, *Evolution's Workshop*, ch. 4.

Livingstone, *Darwin's Forgotten Defenders*.

Numbers, *Darwinism Comes to America*, chs. 1–2.

Questions to Consider:

1. What scientific and philosophical factors led to the rapid and widespread acceptance of the "fact" of evolution following the publication of Darwin's *Origin of Species* in 1859? Did scientists simply want to believe in evolution or did the evidence compel them to accept it?

2. Why did T.H. Huxley's grandson, the Darwinist biologist Julian Huxley, characterize the period around 1900 with the phrase "the eclipse of Darwinism"?

Lecture Five—Transcript
Debates over Mechanism

We have been talking about Darwin quite a bit in the previous two lectures, as well we should. What I want to talk about today are the responses to Darwin's ideas in the late 1800s, which will then set the stage for the debates in the 1900s, which we will talk about in coming lectures.

The theory of organic evolution, that is, that species descended from prior species, quickly found near-universal acceptance among American and European scientists. The first printing of *Origin of Species*, remember that that was 1859, sold out its very first day. Of course, the ground had been prepared, because the year before, Wallace's and Darwin's ideas had been announced. The book was the complete exposition of them. This idea, in its full form as printed in *The Origin of Species*, was widely discussed and debated, critically at first, but increasingly favorably over time. Within a decade after Darwin and Wallace announced their theory of evolution, the idea that species evolved from other species dominated logical thought throughout the United States and Britain. Given the past history of evolutionary ideas, this was a remarkable accomplishment in and of itself.

Central to this conversion was the conviction that the world is governed by natural law, rather than divine caprice. This had been Darwin's principal thrust from the outset, which Lyell had picked up. This was really a methodological change in how science was done, and how people were thinking. Evolutionism fit that transition perfectly. People wanted to look for scientific explanations, naturalistic explanations. Philosophers call it, "methodological naturalism."

The Harvard biologist that we mentioned in the last lecture, Asa Gray, was a devout Christian, and an early Darwin confidant. He worked to smooth reception of Darwinism in America. Darwin and his so-called bulldog, the reporter T.H. Huxley, whom we will talk more about today, were the primary public faces of evolution in England, as was Asa Gray in the United States. He did valiant work getting the idea out, getting it published in leading scientific journals, and getting it announced. Indeed, by 1870, there were really only three principal American naturalists in all of the United States who rejected the basic idea that species evolved from other species. These were led by the great Harvard zoologist Louis Agassiz. There were a couple of others as well, but it was a very small group.

You'll notice that this was only 10 years later. Think of what was happening in America in the meantime. The Civil War, there were lots of distractions going on, and yet that's how quickly the ideas came to dominate. That was largely due to Asa Gray's work in the country. It helped that he was a known Christian, almost an evangelical, certainly a traditional Christian, and that helped smooth the reception.

In England, it was a little rockier. It took a little longer in England, but was essentially complete by about 1880. T.H. Huxley was able to write to Darwin in 1868: "You will have the rare happiness to see your ideas triumph during your lifetime."

By the 1870s and '80s, the primary biologists who held out within the scientific community against the idea of organic evolution were not traditional Christians. That was, of course, shown in America by Asa Gray, whom we mentioned. Rather, these were people who clung to Cuvier's established theories that we talked about way back in the first lecture, that there were successive creations and epochs of geological time. This, rather than the biblical view, was the main opposition within the scientific community. It really shows the remarkable transition that occurred in the way science thought.

Look at the two main opponents. The two most visible opponents against Darwinism in the 1860s and '70s were Louis Agassiz in the United States, and Richard Owen in Great Britain. They would not argue religious or biblical objections to evolutionism. Indeed, neither of them were traditionally religious. They rather argued that complex organs such as the eye, or interdependent species such as flowers and bees, simply could not have evolved by intermediate steps. They must have been designed, because which came first? The bee or the flower? They would both have had to be created together, or neither could function. It was the same way with the eye. How could the eye have evolved? It is so complex, so intricate, that any one of those little changes toward an eye simply wouldn't have any value, and therefore would not have survived by a Darwinian mechanism. These were the sort of arguments they were marshaling, not religious arguments.

The opponents of evolution theory had one other argument, and that was the fossil record. We remember that Darwin was using the fossil record in his own support, by showing the general progression of the fossil record. Cuvier, Agassiz, and Owen had seen progression in the fossil record, but they also saw these breaks in the fossil record. There were jumps. There were lots of missing links. Species didn't seem to just build up over time. Rather, they just seemed to appear in the fossil record without any sort of evolutionary development. This, people like Agassiz and Owen would argue, were arguments against evolution. These people readily accepted a very long geologic history. They would accept that species appeared and disappeared over time. Indeed, it was Agassiz himself who had first discovered the ice ages. He was the first person to think that there were past ice ages. With this general acceptance to science, Agassiz made his name, with evidence that there was widespread glaciation, which would have eliminated vast numbers of organisms.

The point here is that these were not traditionally religious pseudoscientific arguments. These were solid scientific arguments that were being raised against evolution, and that were part of the debate over evolution in the late 1800s. These opponents, such as Agassiz and Owen, never called themselves "creationists," and they never called their ideas "creationism." Agassiz, as I pointed out, was not traditionally religious at all.

Darwin acknowledged the force of these objections. He recognized Agassiz as a formidable opponent, and he once described the eye as "an antidote to atheism." He maintained, however, that more research would prove his theory right, and he called for more research on his ideas.

What happens as we go back as historians of science, and look over what happened to these ideas, it is not that they were won over, but that their proponents simply died out. One by one, these established proponents of what was basically Cuvier's view of successive creations simply got old, retired, or died. They were never replaced by a next generation. Interestingly, all of their students became evolutionists.

The theory of evolution raised a host of interesting new questions, and they quickly came to dominate the research agenda of field naturalists and laboratory biologists. Indeed, some historians of science posit that one of the reasons evolution was so quickly accepted among science is that it posed so many interesting questions to research, because all of these lines of arguments Darwin had laid out, and which were not proofs, but simply arguments, had to have ways found to test those arguments. More evidence needed to be collected to see if it built the case for evolution, or weakened it.

It turned out that once this new generation, this younger generation of naturalists and biologists began looking at organisms with an evolutionary viewpoint, they began seeing more and more evidence of evolution everywhere. Because that's what they were looking for, that's what they saw. What I thought I would do now is to go over some of this scientific evidence that began accumulating during the late 1800s that cinched the case, as it were, that species evolved from other species.

The best scientific evidence of that period, the 1860s, '70s, and '80s, came from highly technical studies of the morphological relationships between species: their function and their structure, their form, the way the species are designed, the way individuals are designed, looking at similarities of structure to see if there were evolutionary ties between animals, and plants to a lesser extent. They began finding all sorts of evidence of evolution in these morphological studies.

For example, biologists began finding evermore rudimentary organs in species. These are organs that no longer particularly serve anything, but are still there, like the appendix or the tailbone. When they began looking at other organisms, and looking for these so-called "mistakes," "spare parts," or unneeded things, they began finding more and more. These made sense under an evolutionary viewpoint, useless holdovers from ancestral forms that would not make any particular sense under creationism.

They also found structural similarities among supposedly related species that had no functional explanation whatsoever. A good example of this that was widely popular at the time was the closer analysis of the flippers of sea mammals such as whales. It was found that the bone structure within the flippers, even though the flippers are complete, is like that of the hand. It has five "fingers." It made no sense as to why there would be a bone structure with five "fingers" built into a flipper that is complete. If sea mammals had evolved from land mammals that had five fingers, and those eventually evolved into flippers, those structures made sense. It doesn't make any particular sense under creationism, but it makes lots of sense in an evolutionary context.

Lunged fishes. They knew there were lunged fishes before, even though nobody ever really thought about them. After evolutionary theory, lunged fishes were seen as a link between true fishes and later, land animals. It made sense under evolution.

The egg-laying duck-billed platypus had always seemed like an odd animal. Marsupials, which raise their young in pouches, such as kangaroos, also seemed odd. What had made mammals distinctive was that of course they give birth to complete young, as opposed to eggs, which are present in reptiles or other similar animals, and fish. Now, however, the egg-laying platypus and the marsupials were seen as a step in evolution from reptiles or birds to mammals. They made sense in evolution. They seemed to be just an idle curiosity for divine creation.

This time, the great German biologist Ernst Haeckel postulated a totally hypothetical being, using the Greek term for "ape-man," "*Pithecanthropus*." He hypothesized that this being would be a link between the simian ancestors, the primate ancestors that evolved into humans, as rather a halfway point, perhaps between apes and humans, and that we should be able to find this "ape-man" in the fossil record. These were the sorts of things that were coming out of morphological studies.

Another area of active scientific research, an area like the morphological studies that had not been too active before Darwin and the theory of evolution dominated, now became an active area of scientific research in the universities of Europe and America.

Another area involved microscopes. Microscopes were getting better and better at this time, with breakthroughs in the technology of lens-making. Using these better microscopes, evolutionary biologists in the laboratory saw evidence of evolution in the study of animal embryos. This would be a second area of proof, or of evidence for evolution that was very active during this period.

Believing in progressive development, Ernst Haeckel and his followers postulated that what he called "higher" organisms, such as mammals, should exhibit simply more embryonic development than "lower" ones. This was his idea, that mammals had evolved further than, for instance, reptiles, birds, fish, or snails. If you look at the embryos of these organisms, there should be relics of their past. This was the theory that he had. We can look back, and if we study them, we should see that if we follow, say, a human embryo, or that of a lamb or calf, it should develop similarly to, for instance, the embryo of a snail fish, or a chicken, and it should simply evolve more. If we study the embryos, then, they should look alike in the early stages. This was called the "recapitulation theory." They should recapitulate past stages of evolution.

Seeing what they wanted to see in the microscopes of those days, and looking at this tiny world of early embryos of different species, during the 1870s and '80s Ernst Haeckel and his followers literally offered what they thought was "proof" of evolution. They tried to picture what they saw, and the pictures they created were of some of these embryos looking quite like early-stage embryos of lower animals, which were quite like the early stages of higher animals. Simply put, the higher embryos continued along similarly, and would just evolve more.

These pictures became widely popular in the textbooks of the day, and were literally offered as proof of evolution. We now know that the pictures were forged, that they saw what they wanted to see. Whether it was out-and-out intentional fraud used to try and prove a theory that Ernst Haeckel believed in, or that he simply saw what he wanted to see and then drew it, we don't know. If you look at those today, however, with the better microscopes of today, this whole theory does not work.

The interesting thing is that it should not work, because Darwinism postulates that there are random inborn variations. They don't occur progressively, but are right there at the beginning. Therefore, the embryos should be different from the very beginning. This is, of course, what we see in embryos today, when we study them. However, Ernst Haeckel believed in a Lamarckian form of evolution, a sort of linear, progressive development. With that sort of theory, they should just progress more. Therefore, he was seeing what he wanted to see, to fit his own type of evolution. I state it because it was so important at the time to convince people that evolution worked. It was very important in historical development, and in persuading people and scientists that evolution worked. It became, literally, one of the best evidences of evolution; though it is not an important one today, historically, it was important.

A third area of development that was widely influential at the time was biogeography. Following Alfred Russel Wallace, biogeographers and naturalists went out to look and see if they could find what he said they would find, and that is, similar species living near other species, as well as to see if the way species are distributed on Earth fit an evolutionary pattern; that evolutionary pattern would be that if the species evolved and developed in say, Australia, it would gradually spread out with different types of related species, spreading out over Australia and then the islands, toward Asia. Then other types of species that had evolved in Asia would spread out from that center, and eventually, both would basically run in to each other. Similarly, this should be true of species evolving out of Africa and Europe. In basic evolutionary thought, species are going to evolve on large land masses, because that's where you have a concentration of plants and animals. You should have species pushing out from different places.

When they looked, that is exactly what they found. The most famous of these is the so-called "Wallace line," named for Alfred Russel Wallace, that divides Asian and Australian species, that runs through the East Indies. You have a basic type, variety, and array of species pushing up from Australia, and others pushing down from Asia. They run into each other in Indonesia. Here you can see, almost going from one island to another, a completely different mix of animals. All of this makes sense with an evolutionary theory of origins. It doesn't make any sense whatsoever under creation. Why would God create certain things here and certain things there? In fact, if you're really literalist about it, they all started from Noah's ark. They should have all just spread out from there, not from different centers of evolution. This became, and remains, important evidence for evolution.

Naturalists also looked for and increasingly found an increasing array of similar species, linking species, that would tie two existing species together, such as two similar species of butterfly or beetle. If they found one species in one area and another species in another, they would begin looking in the area in between to see if they could find a linking species. They often would find one, a sort of intermediate species between the two other types. This was great evidence for evolution, and it showed more and more living connections. Wallace had predicted it, and it was generally found, often found near the contiguous two species.

In addition, biogeographers increasingly found "holdover types," and thought they understood them. They would find certain odd species that no longer survived, because they had not succeeded in the competition. Species like the duckbilled platypus, as we mentioned, or giant reptiles, like giant tortoises. Where did they find these things? They tended to find them in isolated places where the competitors couldn't get to them, on islands, or in Australia—where the stronger mammals that had evolved later, in Eurasia and in North and South America, couldn't get to them. This fit an evolutionary pattern. It has no particular explanation in creationism. Why would God choose to create these odd animals out on islands? Yet, the islands are loaded with odd animals, where they might be protected as relics of evolution.

Finally, an area of activity was the fossil record. Of course, paleontologists who believed in evolution, and even those who doubted, looked to the fossil record. "This should be the best evidence for evolution anywhere, because we should be able to find these fossils that connect up existing types of related species, right back down to the links that tie them together with ancestral types. Find the ancestral types, and then follow those basic types back together."

As they looked around, they found some of them. They never really found a lot, but they found some. Those discoveries helped build the case for evolution. Indeed, pointing toward these finds, the American paleontologist Edward Drinker Cope in 1872 declared that evolution was an "ascertained fact."

But there was a fly in the ointment for Darwin in all of this. Evolution was being increasingly accepted by scientists. It was nearly universal by the time of Darwin's death. There was much less acceptance, however, of his mechanism of the idea of natural selection as the force that drove the process. Indeed, evidence and interpretations mounted against natural selection.

Now, as originally conceived by Darwin and Wallace, the natural selection of random variations, small, random variations in every offspring, would lead to evolution. Under prevailing notions of inheritance, however, this sort of thing just didn't work. It didn't work because even if you had a beneficial variation, for instance, a rabbit that was a little faster and that could better escape the hawk, when that rabbit bred, it would have to breed with another rabbit. Under notions of inheritance of the time, before modern genetics, the idea was that the offspring would tend to be in between, so that the faster rabbit would mate with another rabbit, and the offspring would tend to be somewhere in between the two rabbits in their ability, only half as fast. That "half as fast" rabbit would have to breed with a regular rabbit, and the next generation would only be one-quarter as fast. Any beneficial variety would literally be swamped into the species' norm, and be pulled back into the mainline of the species. Therefore, scientists would argue, little variations should not have led anywhere, at least according to the prevailing theory of inheritance.

That was one problem with natural selection. Another problem involved the physical sciences of the time, before the discovery of radiation, uranium, and other forms of power. They tried to estimate how old the Universe could be, and how old the solar system would be, how long the sun would keep burning. The estimates by very highly-respected physical scientists were that the solar system could not to be more than about 200 million years old. Otherwise, the sun would have just burned out in that length of time. 200 million years did not give enough time for natural selection's minute changes to accumulate over time. It didn't give enough time for that to produce the array of life that they had found. Even Darwin agreed with that. It couldn't operate that fast.

Further, many scientists, including Wallace, denied that the natural selection of random variations could lead to major jumps in human intelligence, or in the human morality that seems to separate humans from other animals. "We are just too different from the rest of animals to have evolved in this process." Even Wallace gave credibility to that theory.

Finally, there was the continued evidence of gaps in the fossil record. They convinced some scientists that whatever process generated the evolutionist species, in that they still believed that species evolved from other species, it must somehow operate in spurts and stops. It must be able to speed up, somehow. It couldn't be that gradual, or the fossil record would have more connecting links. If it went really fast, though, not many of connecting links would get laid down, because it would be pretty rapid.

That raised problems with the theory of natural selection. Indeed, these problems were so profound that even Darwin and Wallace increasingly sought other evolutionary mechanisms to supplant natural selection, and perhaps because of this, he did a funny thing. As I said, he published *Origin of Species* in 1859. He kept revising it, however. You have to look at the particular edition of *Origin of Species* to know what it says. He brought out almost a dozen editions of *Origin of Species* over the next 20 or so years after the publication of the original; all of them were a little different, and if you look back at the original, it is very Darwinian. It is the account of Darwinian evolution that we know today. If you read the last one, however, you would think that you were reading Lamarck. It is so Lamarckian. It includes so many Lamarckian ideas. He changed his own ideas to meet these scientific objections. He still remains an evolutionist, but the mechanism changes in his own work.

If we go back now and examine what was developing, he would see that though there were a lot of permutations, there were three basic alternatives to classical Darwinism that developed during the late 1800s. As I mentioned with Darwin already, one was Lamarckian evolution; it was actually in revised form, and was known as "neo-Lamarckian evolution," because it was so updated and revised. It relied on the inheritance of acquired characteristics, modified through use and disuse, to account for the speed and direction of the evolutionary development. These were the ones that Darwin increasingly invoked, because if a species were trying to change to fit changes in the environment, it actually could go faster. This way, you could cram the evolution of species into the available time period, and account for the gaps in the fossil record.

A second one that became widespread, especially in the United States, was a theory called "orthogenesis." This is an odd word. It attributed evolution to internal forces within living things, vital forces that pushed the development of a species in a particular direction, almost like it had a goal, a survival goal within it. Life was viewed as fundamentally different than nonlife for these people, and it was pushing in a particular direction. That would account for the faster process and for the absence of fossils in the fossil record.

A third form of evolution that came up this time was "theistic evolution." It saw God as the source and guide of variations along lines beneficial to the species. This was worked out in its most complete form by Asa Gray, Darwin's main proponent in the United States. Wallace increasingly adopted theistic evolution, at least to explain humans.

These alternatives potentially fit the scientific evidence for the occurrence of evolution without all of the religious and philosophical baggage that comes with natural selection. Theistic evolution and orthogenesis were particularly compatible with the spiritual view, while Lamarckian evolution fit perfectly with the capitalist viewpoint of pulling oneself up by one's bootstraps, and progressing in a direction. Naturally, that is the one that Darwin seemed to like.

By 1900, natural selection had been so discredited that few scientists accepted it as the primary mechanism of evolution. By all accounts, however, every credible biologist in the United States and Western Europe accepted the so-called "fact" of evolution.

Lecture Six
Missing Links

Scope:

Although by 1900 most Western biologists and intellectuals accepted some theory of evolution, popular and religious opposition remained. Technical arguments that appealed to scientists failed to persuade the public, particularly when it came to the notion that humans evolved from apes. The same fossil record that inspired Lamarck and Darwin increasingly became a barrier to popular acceptance of their ideas. Opponents decried the lack of fossils linking either major biological types (such as reptiles and mammals) or humans to their supposed simian ancestors.

Beginning late in the 19th century, those intent on proving the theory of evolution hunted for missing links in the fossil record. Scientific and popular interest focused on finding evidence of prehistoric humans and hominids. Any such "missing links" became front-page news and boosted the popular acceptance of evolution.

Outline

I. Fossils have long been both a principal basis for, and a barrier against, belief in evolution.

   A. Georges Cuvier's early work with fossils suggested that species generally remain constant throughout their lives and are replaced quite suddenly by significantly different forms. Ever since, this pattern has been used as evidence against evolution.

   B. In arguing for uniformitarianism in geology, Charles Lyell countered that fossils were laid down only intermittently; therefore, discontinuities proved nothing. To Lyell, the progressive order of the fossil record suggested gradual change rather than catastrophes.

   C. Building on Lyell's argument, Darwin devoted a chapter in *Origin of Species* to showing that (despite notable gaps) the overall outline of the fossil record supports his theory.

      1. The fossil record displays a basic similarity in the succession of forms in a contiguous area. There is also a tendency toward greater variety and complexity.

2. As unguided natural selection would suggest, there was no fixed rate of change. Some organisms endure; others rapidly change; none reappear.

3. Darwin was confident that once naturalists began looking for them, many of the missing links in the fossil record would be found.

D. During the late 1800s, paleontologists culled the fossil record for evidence of evolutionary development.

1. T. H. Huxley posited that the birdlike legs of some dinosaurs linked birds to reptiles.

2. The discovery during the 1870s of the fossil remains of a feathered reptile called *Archaeopteryx* further linked birds and reptiles.

3. During the 1880s, O.C. Marsh uncovered a complete series of fossils tracing the modern broad-hoofed horse back to a small multiple-toed ancestor.

4. Although such finds satisfied most paleontologists that species evolve, major gaps remained in the fossil record. Anti-evolutionists dismissed the intermediate species as separate creations and pointed to the remaining gap as evidence against evolution.

5. Especially problematic were: (1) the absence of fossils in Precambrian rocks (which suggested that life abruptly appeared at the beginning of the Cambrian era) and (2) the lack of fossils connecting humans to apes.

E. To the extent that some scientists and many non-scientists continued to reject the theory of evolution in the 1890s, their opposition focused on the issue of human evolution. The absence of hominid fossils became a stumbling block to popular acceptance of evolution.

II. Darwin and other evolutionists never claimed that humans descended from apes. Rather, they believed that modern humans and modern apes had a common ancestor.

A. As if to emphasize their differences, Cuvier had placed humans and apes into distinct orders based on differences in their hand and brain structures. Asserting that Cuvier had exaggerated these differences, Huxley now argued that humans and apes belonged in the same order.

B. Huxley offered Neanderthal skulls, first found in Germany in 1856, as a possible ape-like hominid but ultimately acknowledged that, with a cranial capacity equal to that of a human, the Neanderthal could not come from a species linking humans with smaller brained ancestors.

C. As late as the 1850s, Lyell cited the absence of ancient human fossils to support man's recent creation. In his 1863 book, *The Antiquity of Man*, he drew on new archaeological evidence to greatly push back the supposed first appearance of humans.

D. Accumulating archaeological evidence pointed to a long history of human cultural development, which such evolutionists as Huxley and Ernst Haeckel saw as evidence for the biological evolution of human races. Haeckel's views reflected his belief in an extreme racist variant of Lamarckism that later influenced Nazi thought.

III. Dutch physician Eugene Dubois set out to "prove" evolution by finding fossil evidence of the missing link between apes and humans.

    A. Born in 1858 in the conservative Catholic southeastern provinces of the Netherlands, Dubois consciously rejected religious superstition for scientific truth.

        1. A brilliant and driven boy, Dubois sought to advance science and discredit religion.

        2. He accepted a materialist form of Lamarckian evolution through reading Haeckel and Huxley, studied medicine in Amsterdam, and became a teacher there.

        3. Following Haeckel, Dubois conducted morphological studies of the larynx, looking for physical evidence of human evolution in the origins of speech, but he became bored with the study. He wanted to find more dramatic proof of human evolution.

    B. In 1887, Dubois abandoned a promising academic career and, with his young family in tow, became an army physician in the Dutch East Indies.

1. Although Darwin and Huxley proposed that humans evolved in Africa, Dubois convinced himself that it happened in the East Indian islands then ruled by the Netherlands. He aimed to find hominid fossils among the orangutans there.

2. Unable to obtain funding for his project, Dubois became an army physician and devoted all of his free time to searching caves and river valleys for fossils.

3. In 1892, after five years of searching on two islands, native workers digging under Dubois's directions in a canyon on Java uncovered the skullcap, thigh bone, and teeth of a hominid that Dubois named *Pithecanthropus* in honor of Haeckel.

C. Popularly known as "Java Man," *Pithecanthropus* was sensational but controversial.

1. Its distinguishing characteristics were an intermediate-sized brain case and an upright posture. This fit Darwin's prediction that an upright posture (which freed the hands for carrying and using tools), rather than a big brain, led to human evolution.

2. After initial interest, paleontologists generally dismissed Dubois's claims of the great age and ape-like character of his fossils. Back in the Netherlands, Dubois became reclusive and refused to show the fossils to critics.

3. Preferring to see brain development as the cause of human evolution, paleontologists embraced the 1912 fossil discovery of a big-brained hominid in Piltdown, England. Until discredited in 1953, "Piltdown Man" confused the story of human evolution.

IV. Beginning in the 1920s and increasingly in the last half of the 20th century, fossil evidence of human evolution captured the popular imagination.

A. At first, these fossils came from South Africa.

1. In 1925, Raymond Dart identified the fossil remains of an earlier human ancestor, which he named *Australopithecus africanus*. Much older and smaller brained that Java Man, it walked upright and had humanlike teeth.

2. In 1936, Dart's disciple Robert Broom found more *Australopithecus* fossils, but apparently of a later type, *A. robustus*. These finds fit the linear pattern of human evolution typically associated with Lamarckism.

B. Beginning in 1929, more fossils like those from Java were found in China, with the group later reclassified as *Homo erectus*, an early human type.

C. Beginning in the 1950s, East Africa became the primary source of early hominid fossils.

1. The Leakey family and Donald Johanson, leading well-funded research teams, uncovered fossils of various overlapping *Australopithecus* species, some older and some younger than the ones from South Africa.

2. In 1961, Mary Leakey found fossil evidence of an older species of humans, *Homo habilis*, that lived among later types of *Australopithicus* in East Africa up to 1.8 million years ago. *H. habilis* used tools and had a human-sized brain.

3. A branching pattern of hominid evolution took shape in accord with Darwinism.

4. During the 1990s, paleontologists found fossils they assigned to two new hominid genuses, *Ardipithecus* and *Orronrin*. Estimated at up to 6 million years old, these individuals had small brains but erect posture.

D. The evolutionary tree for humans is now as complete as for any type of animals, and it fits a Darwinian pattern. Upright posture came first, presumably because it had survival value in a changing environment, then bigger brains and tool use.

E. New finds of hominid fossils still generate front-page news around the world. As Dubois predicted, these fossils now serve as the most well known evidence for evolution.

Essential Reading:

Bowler, *Evolution*, chs. 7–8.

Supplementary Reading:

Dart, *Adventures with the Missing Link*.

Eddy and Johanson, *Blueprints*, ch. 18.

Larson, *Summer for the Gods*, ch. 1.

Shipman, *Man Who Found the Missing Link*.

Questions to Consider:

1. How could 19th-century scientists draw such differing conclusions about evolution from the same fossil evidence?

2. Why has there been such widespread public interest in fossil evidence for human evolution?

Lecture Six—Transcript
Missing Links

Hello, and welcome back. We had been talking in the last lecture about the late 19th-century developments and debates over evolution and natural selection. During those discussions, I have often mentioned fossils. In fact, in all of the lectures, fossils keep coming up, so I thought I would step back and take one lecture here, and talk about the major role that fossils have played in the debate over evolution and natural selection, really from the very beginning, but carry it on up through this crucial period, the turn-of-the-century period that we are at right now in the history of evolutionary thought.

Fossils have long been both the principal basis for, and the barrier against, belief in evolution. They have played both roles. That is why they are so central to the issue. George Cuvier's early work suggested that species generally remained constant throughout their lives. This was from his work with fossils, primarily. Because he looked at the fossil record, he saw fossils appearing suddenly in the fossil record. That is, a particular type of species suddenly appeared in the fossil record, remained distinct throughout its period, and then ended abruptly. Ever since, this pattern that Cuvier established in the fossil record has been constantly present. Because it is in the fossil record, this pattern has been used as evidence against evolution.

When he argued for uniformitarianism in geology, as we've seen, Charles Lyell countered that fossils are only laid down intermittently, when the environment is right for doing so. Therefore, discontinuities within the fossil record prove nothing at all. To him, and others like him, the progressive order of the fossil record suggested that gradual change occurs in species. It doesn't give evidence of catastrophes, as it did with Cuvier.

Building on Lyell's argument, Darwin devoted an entire chapter in *The Origin of Species* to taking an area of weakness, and making it an area of offense. It was a good strategic move. He used the chapter to show that despite notable gaps in the fossil record where discontinuities were present, and new fossils appeared abruptly, the overall outline of the fossil record supported his theory, because it is progressive. Indeed, there are two major reasons as to why the fossil record supports his theory, and he argued them.

First, the fossil record displayed a basic similarity in the succession of forms within a contiguous area. That is, if you would go to any one particular area and study the fossils of it, you would basically see similar types of fossils over time. If you would go to another area, you would see basically similar types of fossils over time. This is a sort of evolutionary pattern of development. Within those areas, there is a tendency toward greater variety of those basic types, such as catlike species, or deer-like species, or a particular type of fish or bird, etc., as well as increasing complexity. This is an evolutionary progression.

A second argument that he would make is that as unguided natural selection should suggest, there is no fixed rate of change. Some organisms endure over vast periods of geologic history in the fossil record. Others change rapidly, and never does a fossil reappear. Once a species is in the fossil record, it disappears out of the fossil record, and does not reappear later in the fossil record. This suggests a kind of natural selection approach to evolution, as opposed to a neo-Lamarckian approach, or some of the other versions that we have talked about. There are different rates of change, based upon a species' survival ability. They come and go over time.

He saw those as evolutionary patterns, and as patterns suggested by natural selection. Darwin was confident that once naturalists began looking for them, many of the missing links in the fossil record, those gaps when fossils of a particular species appear abruptly, those "missing links," would be found. He argued in *Origin of Species* that no one had been looking for them before. They were not what people had expected.

Of course, after *Origin of Species*, and after most biologists became evolutionists, they immediately began looking for the missing links. Indeed, not only the proponents of evolution for the missing links did so, but opponents of evolution as well looked closely at the fossil record to find evidence supporting one or the other. From the time *Origin of Species* was first published clear through to today, fossils have been a battleground where people interested in the theory have focused their attention.

In a way, the fossils provide the only evidence we have of an historical snapshot of the past. We can use plenty of evidence today to argue for and against evolution, but if we want a historical record, the fossils provide our best clue. That's why they have been a center of attention.

After the publication of *Origin of Species*, in the late 1800s paleontologists culled the fossil record for evidence of evolutionary development. This is where T.H. Huxley came in most notably. We talked about him before. He was called "Darwin's bulldog," and was a main propagandist for evolution. In his area of research, however, he focused mostly on paleontology and fossils. That is where he was bringing up new work, in addition to his rhetorical work as a speaker and as a witty proponent of evolution theory.

T.H. Huxley looked for evidence of what these missing links were. He came up with a variety of them, but one is that he posited the work on dinosaurs. He saw that some dinosaurs had birdlike legs. These tended to be the dinosaurs that ran fast across the plains, the smaller dinosaurs. Because some of them had birdlike legs, he posited that might be a link between reptiles and birds. Evolutionists were very interested in finding these links between major types of beings, such as birds and reptiles, or fish and land animals. He had an even better one that he popularized, though he did not discover it. During the 1870s, the fossil remains were found of a feathered reptile called "*Archaeopteryx*." This bird or reptile, whichever it was, a reptile with feathers, had fossil remains found in several places. For many people, this became a key link. It was highly publicized. Here was a reptile—which should have scales—with feathers.

During the 1880s, probably the second most important single example of a development from paleontology that would prove evolution, as it were, was discovered by O.C. Marsh, a great American paleontologist. In the American West, he uncovered a complete series of fossil horses, that progressed from a small "toed" horse that had several toes, to the modern horse with a complete hoof. Pictures and reproductions of them still exist at the Smithsonian Institution, and you can look in almost any textbook for O.C. Marsh's examples of the evolution of the horse, from one type to a variety of different types, to the modern type of horse.

Such discoveries satisfied most paleontologists in the late 1800s that species did evolve. This evidence was convincing to them. Major gaps remained in the fossil record. Anti-evolutionists dismissed these intermediate species as separate creations. God could have made a whole variety of horses. They did fit beautifully, though, and they were used as evidence for evolution. Anti-evolutionists could dismiss them, and still point to the vast number of remaining gaps that existed in the fossil record as evidence against evolution.

Just as the evolutionist would point toward the feathered reptile and the horse fossils as evidence for evolution, the anti-evolutionists had things that they could point to as well in the fossil record. They made quite a bit of them. One was the absence of fossils in Precambrian rocks. These are very early rocks from an early epoch, and there are not any fossils in them. This suggested that life abruptly appeared at the beginning of the Cambrian era, and appeared in great complexity and diversity. This suggested creationism. Further, there was a lack of fossils connecting humans with apes. This was important.

A second thing, as we've mentioned before, is that there was nothing more important to creationists than that humans were separately created. Indeed, by the late 1800s, there were many scientists and individuals who were accepting evolution for everything else, but denying the evolution of humans. The lack of, or the missing, links between humans and other animals, were used as evidence that at least, humans were separately created, to the extent that some scientists and many nonscientists continued to reject or limit the theory of evolution in the late 1800s. Their opposition focused on the issue of human evolution. The absence of hominid fossils became a stumbling block to the popular acceptance of human evolution. It was a major issue.

Darwin and other evolutionists had never claimed that humans descended from apes. Rather, they believed that modern humans and modern apes had a common ancestor. This was a highly controversial claim. It gained only grudging acceptance both inside the scientific community and among the general public.

As if to emphasize the differences between humans and any other types of animals, including primates, in the early 1800s Cuvier had placed humans and apes into distinct orders based on differences in their hand structures, which tied in with tool use. One thing that is special about humans is that they use tools. Therefore, you need a particular hand structure, the opposing thumbs, which primates don't have. In addition, the brain structure and brain size differ. Therefore, scientists like Cuvier would look to the large cranial capacity of humans, and the hand structure, to show that humans were fundamentally different. Cuvier used this to place humans, and apes and other primates, in wholly separate orders, not just different genera and species.

Huxley came back and said, "No. Humans belong in the same order as other primates do. They are more closely related than earlier scientists had suggested." Huxley went out and tried to look for something that would connect humans with other primates. The first thing he turned to was the Neanderthal Man, the Neanderthal skulls. The fossil remains of Neanderthals had been discovered in 1850s. They were first found in Germany, and then in other parts of Europe. Huxley initially suggested that this might possibly be an apelike hominid; that is, something that was a connecting link between apes and humans. That appeared in the early works of Huxley shortly after Darwin's *Origin of the Species*.

This attempt broke down; the more they studied the Neanderthal Man, the more they realized that its cranial capacity and brain size were essentially the same as that of humans. Therefore, the Neanderthal could not be a connecting link. They had to do something to find a connecting link. The Neanderthal did not do that.

The thought was that what makes humans distinctly different is their brain size. Fossil remains had to be found of something like a human, but with a smaller brain, smaller cranial capacity.

The interest in this grew. Charles Lyell, the great geologist, had earlier maintained, before the publication of *Origin of Species,* that the absence of ancient human fossils supported man's recent creation. At that time, he believed that all species were separately created—at different times through history, of course.

In 1863, in a book that came out shortly after *Origin of Species*, titled *The Antiquity of Man,* Lyell, now becoming an evolutionist, repainted the picture of human history, and drew on new archaeological evidence that greatly pushed back the supposed first appearance of humans. We see in Huxley and Lyell, two of Darwin confidants, the effort to change man's human history to prepare the way for the acceptance of human evolution. Indeed, accumulating archaeological and anthropological evidence pointed toward a long history of human cultural development. That is, new evidence was found to support the idea that humans had existed a very long time ago, that human civilizations such as the Egyptian, Babylonian, and

Chinese civilizations were very ancient and that before even those times, there were peoples as well, that those peoples had developed gradually over time, and that earlier types of species of humans were much more primitive than current types of humans.

Some of these evolutionists would use the recent anthropological studies from around the world to show patterns that we still see, of those simpler, more primitive humans still existing, such as the natives of Australia, or the people being found in South America, or Africa, or Asia. We see, in the writings from this time, the late 1800s—and this is an important part of evolutionary history—writers like Huxley in England and Ernst Haeckel in Germany, using this evidence of cultural development as a sort of parallel, to show that humans have indeed evolved.

Haeckel himself reflected his beliefs in an extremely racist variant of Lamarckianism—Lamarckianism being the development is linear, from simpler to more complex—to posit that human races themselves reflect this linear development. At this time, examples began appearing in textbooks and various publications of indications of how this development reflected evolutionary development in a very racist form. I've pulled out one comment by Ernst Haeckel, after he wrote a book on the races of man. It was a very influential book historically, because it provided much of the basis for later Nazi thought. He talked about all the differences in the races of man. I will give you a feel for it. When he concludes, and gets to the last race of man, he says:

> "The Caucasians, or Mediterranean man (Homo mediterranous),"

as if the different types of humans weren't all Homo sapiens, but are indeed, different species, and of course, he was talking about the Aryan race here,

> "has from time in memorial been placed at the head of all races of man as the most highly developed and perfect."

Some of these comments are quite frightful today. They were very common in the late 1800s. They were used as arguments for the evolutionary development of humans.

This issue of the evolutionary development of humans, and the lack of missing links, and the way that precluded some people from accepting evolution, drove proponents of evolution almost to distraction. Some of them wanted to prove all of evolution through proving human evolution. Nobody represents that better than the Dutch physician Eugene Dubois.

He set out to prove evolution by finding fossil evidence of the missing links between apes and humans. It is a great example of a scientist with a driven intent who actually finds something, against all odds.

Dubois was born in 1858 in the conservative Catholic southern provinces of the Netherlands. A smart boy, as he grew up, he consciously rejected the "religious superstition," as he called it, of local Catholics in his own family, for scientific truth. Nature lay in science; the truth lay in science.

He was a brilliant and driven boy. He sought to advance science consciously and discredit religion. Nothing would do so better than pushing evolution theory. He personally accepted a very materialistic form of Lamarckian evolution, through his readings of Ernst Haeckel, who was really his idol, as it were, and of T.H. Huxley, whom he admired greatly.

Coming from where he did, and given the options that he had, his best option for a scientific career was to go to Amsterdam and study medicine. He was very successful there. He was a great student, and he became an instructor there, in the University of Amsterdam.

Picking a research project, he decided to follow Ernst Haeckel, and he conducted a morphological study of the larynx. If you think about it, this is a very logical choice. Back then, morphological study, showing connections between different species, was one way that they were trying to establish evolution, through showing similarities in structure.

Picking the larynx was especially telling. He looked at the human larynx, and was trying to compare it with the larynx of primates. What distinguishes humans from other primates? The ability of speech. Thus, he needed to see if he could find out how the larynx could have evolved.

Even though this was a great topic of study, however, the problem was that he was very impatient. He became bored with the study. It didn't prove evolution fast enough, and when he went back home to the southern Netherlands, to this Catholic region, and talked to the priest, the locals, and his father about it, it wasn't convincing enough. It was just a larynx, as it were.

He set about to really try and prove it. What would convince people of evolution? He needed to find the missing link in humans, find the fossil remains, because they were so telling, so convincing, to common people. They always have been. He went out to find this missing link. How was he going to do that?

In 1887, he abandoned a very promising academic career, and with his young family in tow, he became an army physician in the Dutch East Indies. Huxley and Darwin had long proposed that humans must have evolved in Africa. "There are the other primates here; this is the place for humans to have evolved."

Of course, Dubois couldn't easily go to Africa. At that time, Africa was ruled by England and Germany, and was not well-conquered. Conveniently, however, the East Indies were ruled by the Netherlands. He convinced himself that in the Dutch East Indies, the orangutan, the most advanced form of primate, existed. There, he could find the connecting links.

He tried to find governmental support, foundation funding, or donations to support him in going over there and doing a proper research trip, but when he couldn't find it, he was so compulsive and obsessed with the idea, and so convinced that he could prove evolution—in that he had this sense of greatness about him throughout his life—that he became an army physician on the condition that he would get posted in the Dutch East Indies. Then he went over as an army physician with the Dutch army, and devoted all of his free time searching caves and river valleys for fossils, to try to find this missing link that he was convinced was there.

He hired local workers to help him out. He was doing a remarkable job. It passed beyond the stage of a hobby to him to an obsession. The most amazing thing of all was that he actually found a missing link. No one had ever yet found one; people had looked somewhat, but never with the intensity that he did. He was a tribute to dedication. After five years of looking on two different islands, in 1892 native workers digging under his direction uncovered the skullcap, thigh bones, and teeth of a hominid. Dubois gratefully named it in honor of Haeckel as "*Pithecanthropus*."

Popularly known as "Java Man," because that was the island it was discovered on, Pithecanthropus was sensational but controversial. Its distinguishing characteristics were an intermediate brain size between apes and humans, and an upright posture. This fit Darwin's prediction that upright posture, which would free hands for carrying and tool use, rather than a big brain, led to human evolution.

After initial interest, paleontologists generally dismissed Dubois' claims for the great age and apelike character of his fossil. They thought maybe it was just a young human of some type, a native species from the East Indies. Back in the Netherlands, Dubois became reclusive, and began to refuse to show his fossils to his critics.

The problem was that what these people wanted to see, probably because of their pride in being humans, was brain development coming first. The paleontologists wanted to see that. They were thrown off the track in 1912 when an amateur paleontologist found what looked like an upright-walking, big-brained ancestor to humans, in Piltdown, England. The remains were known as "Piltdown Man." For 40 years, this threw things off track, because this was really a forgery that had been put there. Someone had taken bones from animals, and had glued them together with the skull of a human. People thought it was real, because they wanted to think it was real. That threw people off for a while; they wanted to see the brain developing first.

Eventually, however, with further fossil research, researchers were put back on track. That track went right through Java Man. Beginning in the 1920s, and increasingly during the last half of the 20th century, fossil evidence for human evolution captured the popular imagination. First of all, these fossils came exactly from where Darwin expected them to be, from Africa. Indeed, because more research was available there, and because more people were there researching this, the very first fossils came from South Africa. In 1925, Raymond Dart identified the fossil remains of an early human ancestor that he named "Australopithecus africanus." This was much older and smaller-brained than Java Man. It looked like it was in the chain before Java Man. However, it walked upright, and had human-like teeth.

In 1936, Dart's disciple Robert Broom found more fossils of this same basic type, but apparently, of a later variety, to which he gave the species name, "*A. robustus*." These finds fit a pattern typically associated with Lamarckianism, of a linear development, moving from these early species found by Dart and Broom and through Java Man, on up toward humans. At that time, most paleontologists were Lamarckians. This fit the pattern they expected.

Beginning in 1929, more fossils like those from Java were found in China. The entire group was reclassified as "*Homo erectus*," an early human type. This is the name that we still know Java Man by: *Homo erectus*, which came later than the types found by Dart and Broom. Thus, we were getting this development, and it appeared now that humans were hominids. They did start in Africa, and they did spread out, and by the time they got to Java and China, they had evolved to a further species, a fully human species, which were still not *Homo sapiens*, but *Homo erectus*.

Beginning in the 1950s, after World War II, this effort really began to get going, with some finds in East Africa, as opposed to South Africa, which has ever since become the primary source of early hominid fossils.

The Leakey family and Donald Johanson, leading well-funded research teams, quite different than the fate suffered by Dubois, uncovered fossils of various overlapping *Australopithecus* species, some older, and some younger than the ones found in South Africa.

In 1961, Mary Leakey found evidence of an older species of humans, *Homo habilus*. This species of humans lived among later types of *Australopithecus* in East Africa, up to 1.8 million years ago. *Homo habilus* used tools and had an almost human-sized brain. What's appearing from all of this, notice—I use all these names and different types of fossils—is overlapping types, different species, different genera even, overlapping in time and a branching out; this was no longer the linear development predicted by Lamarckianism, but the branching development predicted by Darwinian natural selection.

During the 1990s, paleontologists found even more types of hominid fossils, some of them attributed to yet different genera. Some of them appear to be much older, up to six million years old. These fossils appear to be a species with an even smaller brain size, yet they still walked upright.

The evolutionary tree for humans is now as complete as for any other type of animal. It fits a Darwinian pattern of upright posture coming first—presumably because it had survival value in a changing environment—and then bigger brains, and then tool use. New finds of hominoid fossils still generate front page news around the world. As Dubois predicted, these fossils now serve as the best evidence for evolution.

Lecture Seven
Genetics Enters the Picture

Scope:

Evolutionists were mired in doubts and disagreement at the dawn of the 20th century. Biologists still believed that evolution happened, but there was no consensus among them on how it operated. All the options seemed inadequate, especially classical Darwinism. As often happens in science, answers came from an unexpected source.

Looking for evidence of sustainable evolutionary development though gross inborn mutations, rather than the minute variations posited by Darwin, two separate biologists simultaneously rediscovered the 35-year-old work of Gregor Mendel. Mendelian genetics suggested ways for subtle inborn variations to sustain long-term evolutionary change. Laboratory studies in genetics pushed naturalists' fieldwork from center stage in evolutionary research.

Outline

I. By 1900, divisions among evolutionists over how evolution operated seemed irreconcilable.

  A. Classic Darwinism, which envisioned the natural selection of minute, random, inborn variations of an essentially continuous nature, was widely dismissed as leading nowhere.

  1. Under a continuous view of hereditary variations, as then prevailed, the characteristics of an offspring would be a blending of those of its parents.

  2. Even if an individual with a beneficial variation was more likely to survive, it would likely breed with a "normal" individual, and their offspring would regress toward the species norm. Over time, continuous variations would be "swamped."

  B. Lamarckism, the principal alternative, encountered increasing objections.

  1. Variations are acquired during life. If the reproductive seed is drawn from across the body (via "pangenesis"), as most scientists (including Darwin) then believed, that seed could transmit those acquired characteristics.

2. Despite the plausibility of Lamarckism, proponents failed to produce experimental evidence that acquired characteristics could be inherited, while opponents, such as German cell biologist August Weismann, marshaled opposing evidence.

3. Rejecting pangenesis for the theory of an immutable germplasm transmitting hereditary information, Weismann argued that only inborn traits could be passed on. Stripped of all Lamarckian taints, this was the birth of neo-Darwinism.

4. Lamarckism survived as a scientific theory into the mid-20th century, particularly in the Soviet Union, but gradually lost influence in the West.

C. Around 1900, Dutch botanist Hugo De Vries offered mutation theory as a possible compromise explanation for the evolution of new species.

1. Mutation theory accepted Weismann's position that only inborn traits are inherited.

2. To overcome the concern that inborn variations would be swamped, De Vries postulated that mutations could be significant, discontinuous, and widespread enough to form abruptly a breeding population of a new variety or species.

3. De Vries saw natural selection operating to preserve beneficial mutations.

4. Although interest soon passed as scientists failed to find beneficial mutations, De Vries's idea called attention to the propagation and preservation of discontinuous variations. This laid the ground for rediscovering Mendel's work.

II. Mendelian genetics would provide the basis for reviving Darwinian theories of evolution.

A. During the 1860s, Gregor Mendel (an Austrian monk with an interest in natural history) experimented with the idea of new species as hybrids of old ones. He tested this by crossing distinctly different varieties of pea plants.

1. Rather than producing intermediate varieties, his crosses produced a remarkably regular re-emergence of the parent types.

2. When tall and short pea plants were crossed, the next generation was tall (not mid-sized as predicted by blended inheritance), but in the third generation, three-fourths were tall and one-fourth was short. The same discontinuous pattern appeared for other crosses.

3. Because Mendel's work was mathematical, dealt with discontinuous variations, and involved hybrids, it was largely ignored for 35 years.

4. As long as scientists studied apparently continuous variations, they did not see Mendel's pattern. When De Vries and other scientists accepted discontinuous variations, they rediscovered Mendel's work.

B. Although Mendel's laws were initially associated with major discontinuous variations (or mutations), rather than small continuous ones, their critical significance for salvaging Darwinism ultimately became clear.

1. The mutation theorists who rediscovered Mendel's laws explained them by positing the existence of two "genes" for each trait, with one gene from each parent. The dominant gene would be expressed; the recessive gene would lie dormant.

2. For example, when a pea plant with two tall genes was crossed with one with two short genes, each member of the next generation would be tall (if tall was dominant), but each would carry a short gene that could be transmitted to the third generation.

3. This physical process fit recent microscopic observations of meiosis, in which egg and sperm cells were formed with only half the chromosomes of a normal cell and then were brought together in a fertilized egg cell having the normal number.

4. There would be no blending of characteristics under Mendelian genetics. Beneficial variations would survive without any danger of being swamped.

5. Further, even recessive traits would not be lost permanently. They could reappear in a later generation and be propagated through selection if they were then beneficial.

C. Mutation theorists extrapolated this process to genetic mutations. They postulated that mutations would not be lost through continuous blending and could spread through a population if they were beneficial for survival.

1. In 1910, while studying fruit flies, American genetics pioneer Thomas Hunt Morgan became the first to observe a spontaneous mutation and watch it spread through a breeding population in a Mendelian fashion.

2. His research team later found that mutations could be induced by exposure to radiation and chemicals, suggesting a source for accelerated mutation.

3. With time, geneticists grew to appreciate that this natural process for propagating beneficial gross mutations could also propagate minor variations.

4. Morgan and other Mendelians initially saw mutation alone (without selection) as the source of new species, with natural selection acting only within the normal range of genetic variations in an existing species.

D. Although Mendelian geneticists at first operated in isolation from Darwinian naturalists, their ideas would come together in the neo-Darwinian synthesis of the 1930s.

Essential Reading:

Bowler, *Evolution*, ch. 9.

Supplementary Reading:

Allen, *Life Sciences in the Twentieth Century*, ch. 3.

Eddy and Johanson, *Blueprints*, chs. 5–8.

Mendel, *Experiments on Plant Hybridization*.

Questions to Consider:

1. Why was Mendelian genetics ignored in 1865? Why was it so quickly appreciated after its rediscovery in 1900? What does this change suggest about the nature of scientific discovery?

2. How did Mendelian genetics solve the problem of swamping and, thereby, pave the way for the revival of Darwinian theories of evolution? How did Mendelian genetics undermine Lamarckian theories of evolution?

Lecture Seven—Transcript
Genetics Enters the Picture

Again, we have been talking about 19th-century developments in the debate over evolution, and evolution theory. By 1900, as we've seen, divisions among evolutionists over how evolution operated seemed utterly, totally, irreconcilable. This was called the "period of the eclipse of Darwinism" by Huxley and Huxley's own family. Classic Darwinism envisioned the selection of minute, tiny, inborn, random variations of an essentially continuous nature that were slightly different. This theory seemed to lead nowhere. It was widely dismissed among scientists.

Under the continuous view of hereditary variations, as then prevailed, the characteristics of an offspring would be blended with those of his parents. Even if an individual with a beneficial variation were more likely to survive, it would likely breed with normal individuals of that same species. Therefore, a slightly faster rabbit was surely more likely to survive, this theory says, but it would have to breed with other rabbits, as we've discussed before, and under a blending view of inheritance, their offspring would tend to be somewhere in between. Those offspring may be a little faster, and would again breed with normal rabbits, and be pulled back into the species norm. This was the so-called "swamping problem," that any beneficial variation would be swamped into the species norm, would be drawn into the species norm.

This was an important theory in biology, because obviously, for the most part, species remained the same. This was what kept species constant over time. It was viewed as a major characteristic of species and, under a blending view of inheritance, it discredited any progress coming from classical Darwinian-type evolution.

As we've discussed, the principal alternative was neo-Lamarckianism. By 1900, however, this too was beginning to encounter increasing objections. If you look back into the 1880s and 1890s, everybody was evolutionist, but they tended to be shifting toward Lamarckianism, and away from classical Darwinism. By 1900, even this was coming under fire. Let's think about the problems it was facing.

Under it, variations are acquired during life. The logic of it was that if a reproductive seed was drawn from the entire body via a process known as "pangenesis," which was how most scientists then thought that the reproduction process worked, with the reproductive seed coming from the entire body, and which even Darwin thought was the way, it was logically believed that if the reproductive seed came from the entire body, it would contain parts of the entire body. Thus, an acquired characteristic such as sharper eyes or stronger muscles could contribute to the reproductive seed, and be passed on to the next generation.

Despite the plausibility of Lamarckianism, proponents failed to produce experimental evidence that acquired characteristics could be inherited. Opponents, led by the bombastic German cell biologist August Weissmann, marshaled opposing evidence. That is, it seemed logical, but the experiments, both those done by the proponents who wanted to prove pangenesis and inheritability of acquired characteristics, and those done by its opponents, simply undercut the very theory in every respect.

What Weissmann did was to reject pangenesis for a theory of immutable, what he called "germplasm." Germplasm was the entity that was viewed to be carrying the hereditary information. This germplasm was created at birth, and was not drawn from the entire body. It was separate, distinct, reproductive information, as it were. Whatever an individual of a species was born with would be present forever. That "information" would be passed to the next generation. It wouldn't be influenced by any sort of acquired characteristics. It would only relate to however that individual was born. If that individual, of course, was born with a variation or mutation, that, of course, would pass through. Nothing was acquired during life, however.

Stripped of all Lamarckian taints, this was the birth of neo-Darwinism. It is important to stress this, because this is the intellectual beginning of the current theory of evolution. We are now living in the era of the so-called "neo-Darwinian synthesis," and these are its roots. This is pure Darwinism. It eradicates any issues of acquired characteristics, which of course were throughout Darwin's own publications. Darwin started out with some Lamarckian influence, and by the 1880s, was practically a Lamarckian himself. Weissmann pushed it back to Darwinism; to differentiate from what Darwin himself was saying, it was called neo-Darwinism.

Weissmann was a very creative scientist. His most famous experiment was really a propaganda experiment. He was saying, "Okay, think of Lamarckianism. This pangenesis, this genetic information, comes from the entire body. Is that what you argue? Okay. If that's how acquired characteristics are passed, let me just cut off the tails of mice. I will cut off its tail before it reproduces. If we cut off its tail, obviously," this was a half joking experiment, obviously, but it was very effective, "if pangenesis is pulling the reproductive seed from the entire organism, the entire mouse, if it doesn't have any tail, neither will the next generation." He bred the mice, and of course, the offspring had tails. Then, he cut off the next generation's tails, and their offspring had tails. The tails should have at least been growing shorter, shouldn't they have? By now, they should be turning into guinea pigs. However, they kept their tails for generation after generation.

This was more of a polemic experiment, and yet it was a famous experiment, because it was much-publicized, and while Weissmann did many other experiments, this was the one that captured the public's attention. More than anything, it was used to attack Lamarckianism.

Lamarckianism remained, especially among paleontologists; it was always the strongest there. This was the evidence against it, however, and Weissmann was a wonderful proponent of neo-Darwinism. If there was what experiment that captured the birth of neo-Darwinism, it was Weissmann's experiment with those poor mice back in Germany.

Now, Lamarckianism did survive, as I said, especially among paleontologists, and particularly in the Soviet Union, but it gradually lost its influence in the West. The breakthrough, though, into neo-Darwinism didn't come from Weissmann, even though he helped lay the foundation for it.

The breakthrough occurred around 1900, in the work of Dutch botanist Hugo De Vries, who offered mutation theory as a plausible compromise explanation for the evolution of species. Think of the situation that he was in. Classical Darwinism seemed discredited, because it had no mechanism for preserving variations. Everything seemed to be "swamped." Lamarckianism was discredited by the work of August Weissmann. What was the alternative? Biologists all over Europe and America were scrabbling to try to come up with some answer. If you read scientific papers from this period, you'll just see them struggling with what possibly could be the cause of variation and inheritance, and therefore, evolution. How could the whole process work? "We believe in evolution, but we really don't have a clue of what mechanism is plausible."

De Vries, in this situation, a great botanist, came up with a possible solution, and that was "mutation" theory. When you think about it, it really has its problems, but if you put back in its time, everything had its problems. People were looking for alternatives.

Mutation theory accepted Weissmann's proposition that only inborn traits are inherited. It did have its pedigree coming out of Weissmann's theory of germplasm; many of the early mutation theorists did talk about germplasm as a possible carrying vehicle for these inherited changes. To overcome the concern that these inborn variations would be swamped, De Vries proposed a rather radical solution. He proposed that mutations could be so significant—that they wouldn't be little variations, in other words—the variations would be so significant, the mutations, as it were, so discontinuous, that they would create a big "jump;" not a slightly different color, not slightly better off, not slightly better talons, but dramatically better talons, dramatically changed eyes; dramatic changes.

That was implausible enough, but then he added that they would be widespread enough to happen throughout a population, or at least a significant minority in a population. The affected population would almost abruptly form a breeding population of a new variety of species.

These seem like broad claims, and they were. He was working, though, with primroses. He was a botanist. Primroses, we now know, have a very unstable genetic structure. Therefore, primroses can spontaneously produce great differences, like an entirely different color in the flower. Thus, he was seeing truly remarkable differences in primroses. It comes with the species. He thought that maybe that was happening throughout. To him, natural selection still existed, but it really wasn't central. For him, it operated mostly to preserve beneficial mutations.

Interest soon passed among scientists. It created an initial stir in mutation theory, but within half a generation, interest in mutation theory had pretty well passed. It left a legacy and influence, however. De Vries was a great scientist, and for a while, while people were debating it, even opponents tried to test it. It shifted attention to the propagation and preservation of discontinuous variations—big differences. For this, people were interested in trying to figure out evolution before were thinking either like a Lamarckian or a Darwinian; they were thinking of little changes that would gradually lead in a new direction. Now, for a brief moment in time, they thought about big changes. To an historian of science, that is very important; they began looking for something different, and rediscovered the work of Mendel. It wouldn't have been rediscovered without this refocus on discontinuous variations. Then, in turn, Mendelian genetics would provide the basis for reviving Darwinian theories of evolution.

That forces us back, but first, a little bit about Mendel, here. Gregor Mendel was an Austrian monk of the mid-1800s. He was tremendously interested in natural history; that is, the study of plants, animals, geology. That was his hobby. He had enough free time in the monastery in Austria to pursue his hobby, at least until he was promoted, became the abbot of the monastery, and had to discontinue his works.

During the 1850s and 1860s, however, he was able to pursue his passion for natural history research on his own, in Austria. He experimented with his own ideas. Now, think of the time. The key work took place in the 1860s. Darwin had announced his work, and Mendel had read it with great interest. The focus became, "Where do new species come from?"

Mendel came up with the idea that maybe new species came from a hybrid cross of old, existing species. That was not quite evolution, but if you recall, evolution was in debate. This was shortly after Darwin had published his work. Maybe it was that there were two distinctly different species, and they hybridized or crossed, producing a new species. Maybe that was the origin of species.

He decided to test that theory. He conducted a variety of experiments where he crossbred two different types to see what would happen— two distinctly different types. This was an entirely different chain of experiments. Science often advances in odd directions, with an odd thinker working in odd ways. That was what Mendel was.

Darwin, Weissmann, Huxley, and all of the other people that we've been talking about, and once evolution comes out, Lyell, were thinking about and doing experiments, thinking about things that were just a little bit different. How could they move things along, and keep them moving?

Mendel was jumping with an entirely different idea. He said, "Let's take things that are very different, and see what happens when they come together." Hybrids.

He decided to do some experiments on some easily usable mediums, where it was known that there were greatly different varieties: pea plants. That worked for him, because he had a garden, and could work at it in the monastery. It would have been tough to try to maintain animals and do animal experiments in the monastery. He could do it on the side. They were not going to go anywhere; he did not have to particularly feed them. It was also known that peas, because of farmers' work, came in many different varieties. There were tall pea plants that had been artificially selected, because some people want tall pea plants, and there were short pea plants. Depending on garden space and variety, there were pea plants that produced wrinkled peas, and those that produced smooth peas. There were yellow peas and green peas. There were distinctly different varieties of peas. He could have done the same thing with dogs, but that would have been a lot more work. Peas worked, and also produced a crop, which could also be used to feed the monastery. It was a perfect thing for him to experiment with.

His idea was that if he crossed distinctly different types of peas, they would produce an intermediate variety. The logic was that if you take two species and cross them, you will produce a new species. That was not what he found.

Rather than producing intermediate varieties, his crosses produced a remarkable, utterly unexpected reemergence of the parent types. This totally flew in the face of the established pangenic ideas of blending. With blending, if you crossed two different types, you should have something in between. Everybody just assumed that, but no one had done experiments on it.

He also expected to find that, but he thought he would also find a distinct and maintainable line somewhere in the middle. What he found out, however, was that when you crossed a tall pea plant with a short one, the next generation was all tall, not intermediate. The remarkable thing was that when you crossed members of the second generation together, the third generation produced three-fourths that were tall, and one-fourth that were short. The same discontinuous pattern appeared with other crosses, such as wrinkled versus smooth, or yellow versus green.

Where did this remarkable mathematical relationship come from? How did it know to produce one-quarter and three-quarters in that next generation?

Because Mendel's work was mathematical, and biologists back then, including Darwin, were not mathematical in the way they thought— it was very much a qualitative study back then—because it dealt with discontinuous variations, and scientists were not interested in discontinuous variations, but in slightly different continuous variations, and because it involved hybrids, and nobody else was interested in hybrids because they wanted to see species evolve from other species and not from hybrids, it was largely ignored for 30 years, or even longer, about 35 years, before it was rediscovered in 1900.

It doesn't mean that it wasn't published. It was published in a very good scientific journal. People read it. Mendel even sent a copy to Darwin, oddly enough, saying, "I don't have time to work all of this out, but this might help you in your research." Darwin never even cut the pages and looked at it. He just ignored it.

As long as scientists studied apparently continuous variations, they did not see Mendel's pattern; if you are just dealing with slight differences in your experiments, Mendel's pattern is not going to come up. When De Vries and other scientists, however, accepted discontinuous variations through their work on mutation theory, they immediately rediscovered Mendel's work. This was no surprise; it was published in good journals. When De Vries went to write up his research, he did a literature search, as any good scientist would do. Of course, he turned up Mendel's work. Other mutation theorists, just by doing this, uncovered Mendel's work, read it, and it was as if the veil had been lifted. Suddenly, things made sense that hadn't made sense before.

Although Mendel's laws were originally associated with major discontinuous variations or mutations, such as his distinctly different pea plants which were tall versus short, rather than small continuous ones, which was what was going to be ultimately necessary for neo-Darwinian evolution and its application there, their critical significance for salvaging Darwinism ultimately became clear over time.

The mutation theorists who rediscovered Mendel's work tried to figure out, in their effort to explain them, what possible physical reality out there in nature, in these pea plants, could produce such weird results. What could really be happening in the pea plants, to have produced this three-quarters/one-quarter relationship? What physical reality could produce that?

Mendel hadn't thought about that. He had not worked on that to a great extent. When the mutation theorists got hold of it, however, they explained it by positing the existence of two things they called "genes." This is an important word for the 20th century. It comes right from the beginning of the 20th century.

They tried to explain how Mendel came up those results. "Let's posit that there are two genes for each trait, not one, and that every trait in every individual comes from two genes, one gene from each parent. The dominant gene is expressed, and the recessive gene will lie dormant."

That was the underlying way that they understood this underlying physical reality. It's easiest to give you an example. For example, when a pea plant with two tall genes (the tall pea plants Mendel experimented with were consistently tall, so there were two tall genes), as Mendel was working with, was crossed with one that had two short genes (the short pea plants Mendel experimented with were consistently short, so there were two short genes), the next generation will have one gene from each parent. Therefore, there would be one tall, and one short gene.

If tall is the dominant characteristic, all the plants would be tall, but the second generation would carry the short gene in it. The tall would be expressed, the short would be recessive, and that generation would be a kind of "carrier" of shortness.

If each of those plants were crossed from the second generation, each would have one tall, and one short. If you work out the numbers, the chances are that when those two would cross, there would be a 25 percent chance of two tall, a 50 percent chance of one tall and one short, and a 25 percent chance of producing two short. What would happen in the next generation? The tall would be dominant, with three talls and one short. That was the physical reality they saw underlying Mendel's work. It fit recent laboratory discoveries in working with the reproductive process.

Microscopes were getting better and better at this time, and scientists had actually observed the process of meiosis, in which an egg and sperm cells are formed, or offspring cells, reproductive cells, are formed. They had literally seen in this process that the egg and sperm cells had only half the chromosomes of a normal cell. Then, when a sperm and egg cell were united to produce a fertilized egg, half of the chromosomes from each were reunited, so the final offspring would have the normal number. You could see how this fit the physical reality they were talking about, if you posit that each chromosomes carried a number of genes.

Under this, there would be no blending of characteristics, no blending under Mendelian genetics. Beneficial variations would survive without any danger of being swamped. Faster rabbit? That offspring would have the "faster rabbit" gene, as would their offspring, and therefore, they would produce either the faster rabbits, or, if they bred with a normal rabbit, some offspring would have the faster, some would have the slower. What would survive? The faster ones would survive; they would not be swamped back. They would maintain their variation.

Further, even recessive traits would not permanently be lost. They would continue to survive, even if conditions were not favorable, because they would be recessive traits. If the dominant was expressed, in, for instance, the rabbits, some of them would still carry the recessive traits, but they would survive, if the faster was dominant.

Then, if conditions changed, so that the recessive trait was beneficial to that generation, it could be propagated through selection. Think of pea plants. If there is a situation where tall is beneficial because of light, because of trees or some other element, the tall pea plants would survive by natural selection, you would get more tall pea plants. If there were shortness in them, however, the short ones might die out and tall ones live because of the conditions, but some of those would retain the short gene. If conditions changed, and the environment was dry so that short plants were better because they are low to the ground, the situation would gradually reverse, with tall plants dying out and short ones surviving, so that the short ones would dominate. They could adapt and evolve to fit the environment.

Now, of course, Mendel was working with mutations he found in the existing population. He wasn't dealing with changes, with new varieties. He was dealing with conditions that were already in existence, tallness or shortness in the pea plants. You could see how existing genetic difference could lead to evolution from using Mendel's work.

However, what mutation theorists add to that is that they extrapolated on Mendel's process to the situation of a genetic mutation or variation. This is where a change occurs so that an offspring has a new inherited difference. Using Mendelian-type logic, they postulated that mutations would not be lost through continuous blending, and if there was a variation that was beneficial to survival, that variation could spread throughout the population. The question was: Could they show it? Could they prove it?

They looked around, breeding different species, to see if they could happen upon a natural chance variation, and then to see if that natural chance variation could be propagated in a Mendelian way. If it could be propagated in a Mendelian way, it would be a basis for that evolution to occur, that change to occur in and be passed on to other generations. If it was beneficial, it could spread throughout a population, and create the evolution of species, the origin of species, as it were.

With a variety of scientists working in various places, the breakthrough came in 1910. It came by studying fruit flies, which are wonderful things to study, because unlike pea plants or people, they have lots of generations; they don't live very long, and you can follow a generation in about 10 days. You can see new generations, and easily study them over time.

An American genetics pioneer, one of the truly great scientists of the 20th century, Thomas Hunt Morgan, became the first to observe a spontaneous mutation. In his case, it was a red-eyed fruit fly. A fruit fly had just been born with red eyes. He was able to observe that mutation and watch it spread throughout a breeding population in the Mendelian fashion. The percentages worked out for a mutation, as well as for an existing genetic variation that was already inside the population.

His research team later found out that mutations, like red eyes in fruit flies, or extra wings, or other mutations, could be induced by exposure to radiation, or exposure to chemicals. This was important, because it suggested a source for accelerated variations, and therefore, speeding up evolution. Say the Earth's protective layers changed, and more radiation came through from the sun, or there was a sunspot that created extra radiation, or there was a volcano that spewed forth chemicals, you could have times of accelerated mutation, accelerated genetic variation, and that could speed up the evolutionary process. Of course, back then, they were concerned with how to make the actual evolution that we see fit the fossil record, and fit the time available. They still are.

With time, geneticists grew to appreciate that this natural process for propagating beneficial growth mutations could also work to propagate minor, tiny, very small, seemingly continuous variations. Morgan and other Mendelians initially saw mutation alone without natural selection as a source for new species, with natural selection acting only within the normal range of genetic variations of existing species.

Although Mendelian geneticists at first operated in isolation from Darwinian naturalists, their ideas would come together to form the neo-Darwinian synthesis of the 1930s. That synthesis, however, deserves a lecture all its own.

Lecture Eight
Social Darwinism and Eugenics

Scope:

Evolutionary thinking in biology spilled over into social thought. Even before Darwin published his theory in 1859, Herbert Spencer promoted the idea of a survival-of-the-fittest process driving social progress. With the rise of Darwinian biology, such thinking gained credence under the banner of "social Darwinism." Theories about how humans evolved increasingly influenced ideas of how people should live. Competition appeared beneficial.

Coupled with a rudimentary appreciation of genetics, social Darwinism fostered the eugenics movement, a social crusade advocating more children from genetically "fit" parents and fewer children from genetically "unfit" ones. Proponents typically equated fitness with intelligence, but they often favored physical strength, health, and beauty, as well. Some of their methods were voluntary, but many nations and most American states enacted at least some compulsory eugenic laws before the movement was discredited by Nazi practices during World War II.

Outline

I. Coined by its critics, the term "social Darwinism" gained currency during the Victorian era as a catch-all phrase to identify various utilitarian philosophies and policies that attributed human progress to unfettered competition among individuals.

   A. Valuing competition fit the spirit of the day. It predated Darwinian biology.

   1. In the late 1700s, Adam Smith argued that economic progress depended on individual initiative. His faith in the natural harmony of human interactions gave him hope that all people would benefit from laissez-faire capitalism.

   2. Embracing the idea of laissez faire, by 1800, Thomas Malthus noted that because of natural limits in resources, any social competition would have losers as well as winners. He saw that a "struggle for existence" fostered the general good by weeding out the weak.

3. Malthus's thinking inspired Darwin to conceive of natural selection as the engine of biological evolution, but he did not publish his views until 1858.
4. Beginning in the early 1850s, English philosopher Herbert Spencer popularized a Malthusian view of individual and group competition. He hailed the "survival of the fittest" as the only sure foundation for human progress.
5. With the advent of Darwinism in biology, Spencer's views of social development became known as social Darwinism even though Darwin did not fully endorse them.

B. Social Darwinism encouraged laissez-faire capitalism and discouraged helping the "weak" in an era of widespread industrialization and urbanization.

1. Spencer maintained that government should never interfere in domestic economic or social affairs. Business regulation slowed progress, he said, while public health and welfare programs simply harmed people in the long run.
2. Under the banner of "root, hog or die," Yale economist W. G. Sumner argued that nature eliminates inefficiency and that any interference would backfire.
3. Such Gilded Age industrialists as Andrew Carnegie, John D. Rockefeller, and James J. Hill publicly justified their business practices in social Darwinist terms.
4. Opponents of public health and welfare programs drew on social Darwinist thinking in shaping American and European public policy throughout the late 1800s.
5. Biological Darwinists did not necessarily accept social Darwinism (with some, such as Alfred Russel Wallace, arguing that humans could guide their own evolution), but social Darwinists did use biological Darwinism to justify their views.

II. For many late 19th-century Europeans and Americans, the most important area of competition was between races and among nations. Social Darwinism was invoked to justify Western imperialism, colonialism, militarism, and scientific racism.

A. Racism predated Darwinism, but biological evolution appeared to justify it.

    1. Lamarckism posited a hierarchical view of progressive development, with more "civilized" races seen as more biologically advanced.

    2. Despite Darwin's view of evolution as branching rather than linear, most 19th-century Darwinists saw a single line of human development, with Northern Europeans having evolved the farthest because of conditions in the locations they lived.

    3. Both of these views inevitably blurred notions of cultural and biological evolution.

    4. Darwin and Spencer believed that racial struggle contributed to human evolution by "superior" races replacing "inferior" ones where they mixed. Darwin subtitled his 1859 book *or the Preservation of Favored Races in the Struggle for Life.*

    5. At the time, such views justified European colonization of Asia and Africa. They led many European-Americans to believe that Indians and Negroes would die out in the United States.

B. For some, social Darwinism called for militaristic competition among nations.

    1. Beginning in the late 1800s, Germany's leading Darwinian biologist, Ernst Haeckel, argued that nations and races advance through competition. An ardent nationalist, he advocated a strong, united Germany to dominate the world.

    2. Haeckel's social Darwinism contributed to German militarism leading up to the First World War. Germany's defeat in that war embittered Haeckel and his followers.

    3. Convinced of the biological superiority of the German people, some of Haeckel's followers contributed to the rise of Nazism and its policies of racial purity.

III. Combined with Mendelian genetics, social Darwinism led to the eugenics movement.

    A. Shortly after Darwin published *Origin of Species*, his cousin, Francis Galton, conceived of applying its teachings to human development.

        1. As in other species, Galton argued, fit humans produce fit offspring and unfit humans produce unfit offspring. As a thinking species, humans can use this understanding to accelerate the evolutionary process through selective breeding.

        2. Galton defended his theory with surveys purportedly showing that ability and success ran in some families while inability and failure ran in others. He linked intelligence, beauty, and health with ability; ignorance, ugliness, and sickness with inability.

        3. In 1883, Galton coined the term "eugenics" to designate polices and programs designed to encourage more children from the fit and fewer from the unfit.

    B. Eugenics attracted widespread interest after the 1900 rediscovery of Mendelian genetics.

        1. Genetics appeared to offer a physical basis for Galton's theories. Many experts saw such traits as mental illness and retardation, epilepsy, and criminality as the products of easily eliminated simple hereditary factors.

        2. At a time when science was held in high esteem, eugenics offered a scientific methodology for the social sciences. Nature all but replaced nurture in social scientific thought. The intelligence quotient (IQ) was invented as an objective measure of intelligence.

        3. Sociologists conducted public health surveys and compiled family pedigrees showing a hereditary basis for crime, poverty, anti-social behavior, and low IQ.

        4. Although eugenics never gained broad popular support, many scientific, professional, and philanthropic organizations promoted its acceptance. These efforts influenced public policies throughout the United States and Europe.

C. "Positive eugenics" sought more children from the fit.
1. Winston Churchill, Theodore Roosevelt, and other prominent politicians openly worried that the professional classes were not reproducing in sufficient numbers. Progressive sociologist Edward A. Ross called it "race suicide."
2. Educational efforts taught students the importance of eugenic mate selection and the civic duty of having children. Pre-existing anti-miscegenation law was revived.
3. Eugenic societies held "fitter family" and "eugenic baby" contests.
4. Eugenic fitness was proposed as a prerequisite for marriage and adopted as a policy by some liberal Protestant churches. Some countries adopted tax and employment policies to encourage able citizens to have children.

D. "Negative eugenics" sought fewer children from the unfit.
1. Every American state and most Western countries adopted polices of sexually segregating certain supposedly dysgenic classes, typically the mentally retarded.
2. Thirty-five American states and many European countries instituted compulsory programs of sexual sterilization for the mentally ill and retarded, habitual criminals, or epileptics. Germany's program was later extended to include Jews.
3. During the period from 1900 to 1960, some 60,000 Americans were sterilized under compulsory state programs. Such programs were upheld as constitutional by the U.S. Supreme Court in 1927.
4. Partly on eugenic grounds, Congress curtailed immigration by non-Nordic stock.
5. Nazi Germany moved from eugenic sterilization to euthanasia. German geneticists actively supported racial purity programs. Biologists joined the Nazi Party at a higher rate than any other professional group.

E. Except for the Catholic Church, opposition to eugenics was disorganized and ineffective until the late 1930s, when Nazi practices discredited all such efforts.

    1. Beginning in the 1930s, social scientists increasingly looked to environmental causes of human behavior. Nurture replaced nature in social scientific thought.

    2. More slowly, geneticists recognized the complexity of human heredity. Simple eugenic remedies were abandoned as ways to deal with multi-factorial traits.

    3. By the end of World War II, social Darwinism appeared morally bankrupt.

Essential Reading:

Bowler, *Evolution*, ch. 10.

Supplementary Reading:

Hofstadter, *Social Darwinism in American Thought*.

Kevles, *In the Name of Eugenics*.

Larson, *Sex, Race and Science*.

Paul, *Controlling Human Heredity*.

Questions to Consider:

1. Is it fair to blame Charles Darwin for social Darwinism? How much did biological Darwinism contribute to racism, imperialism, colonialism, and militarism?

2. Why did early 20th-century public policy makers so readily accept radical scientific solutions (including eugenic sterilization) for traditional social problems (such as crime)? Did this reflect undue faith in science?

Lecture Eight—Transcript
Social Darwinism and Eugenics

Hello, and welcome back. We have been talking mostly about science in these lectures, but this particular science, as we all know, had profound social implications. Those social implications came forth not too long after Darwin published his ideas, in the late 1800s, and blossomed in the early 1900s, under the general rubric or term of "social Darwinism." Actually, this term, social Darwinism, was coined by critics, but it gained currency even by its proponents during the Victorian era as a catchall phrase to identify various utilitarian philosophies and policies that attributed human progress to unfettered competition among individuals. That was the basic core of the idea.

Valuing competition as a great good fit the spirit of the day, and predated Darwinian biology. Think back. In the late 1700s, Adam Smith argued that economic progress depended on individual initiative—not governmental regulation, not social networks, but individual initiative. His faith in the natural harmony of human interaction gave him hope that all people would benefit from laissez-faire capitalism; that is, unfettered capitalism. This was unregulated capitalism. The name associated with it was "laissez faire."

Embracing the idea of laissez faire, by 1800 Thomas Malthus, about whom we have already talked quite a bit, noted that due to natural limits on resources, there would be losers as well as winners in social competition. This set him off somewhat from Adam Smith. Yet, he embraced the theory, embraced the idea, recognized that there would be losers, but he saw the struggle for existence as fostering the general good by weeding out the weak. As painful as it might be to some, in the long run, this was for the best.

As we've seen, Malthus's thinking inspired Darwin to conceive of natural selection as the engine for biological evolution. Even though Malthus inspired Darwin in the 1830s, Darwin held off from publishing until 1858.

Showing how much this fit the spirit of the day, however, even before Darwin published his ideas or announced them, other thinkers began catching up with him. Beginning in the early 1850s, the very influential English philosopher Herbert Spencer popularized a Malthusian view of individual and group competition. Indeed, he is the one, even before Darwin, who coined the term "survival of the fittest" that was later so much associated with Darwinian thinking. He hailed the struggle for survival and survival of the fittest as the only sure foundation for human progress. Now, Herbert Spencer was mostly a thinker in existing populations of people. He wasn't talking about animals in general, or evolution of plants or other organic species. He was talking about how the human races—how people—progress.

With the advent of Darwinism in biology, Spencer's views on social development became known as "social Darwinism," rather than, say, "social Spencerianism." In this Darwin did not fully, at least publicly, endorse them; although he inclined to those directions privately, he stayed out of a lot of those debates. Spencer continued to write, and many people would characterize him as the most influential philosopher in the English-speaking world of the late 1800s. Yet, the ideas are called "social Darwinism." This was probably because biology carried so much credibility, and tying them to biology rather than just the social sciences gave them more credibility in their own areas.

Social Darwinism encouraged laissez-faire capitalism, and discouraged helping the "weak," as they were called, in an era of widespread industrialization and urbanization. This is what characterized this period. This was when England, the United States, and Western and Northern Europe, especially, were being transformed from agricultural lands, where most people lived on farms and took care of their families, to an area where most people were thrown together in cities. There wasn't the social support network, the familial networks, the kinfolk to take care of people. Often, people had moved off the farms and were not living near extended family. If they were living with their families, people had to leave the home and go off to a factory to work, or to an industry of some sort.

Therefore, family members were not at home to take care of people. On the farm, this sort of thing could be taken care of. This provided the world that we see when we read Dickens novels, or some of the muckrakers in American literature, pointing out the plight of urban life, the plight of industrial life. An important question people had was that this problem was so visible, the problem of homelessness, the problem of people who had mental or physical disabilities. How would they work in cities, when it was pretty obvious that they could get along on the farms? Suddenly, there were new demands in the city. There weren't the social networks to take care of them. Was government going to move in and fill these gaps? Were taxes going to be raised to provide welfare, and social support networks that were now becoming necessary in an industrialized and urbanized world?

These were important debates in England and in the United States, in Germany, in France, in the late 1800s and early 1900s. This is where Spencer's ideas on social Darwinism had an impact.

Spencer maintained that government should never interfere in domestic, economic, or social affairs. He maintained that business regulation simply slowed progress. While it might protect people here and there, ultimate social progress required that the businesses be able to operate freely, and let the buyer beware; let the consumer operate, let business progress.

He also maintained that public health and welfare programs simply harmed people, over the long run. How could they harm people? They harmed people by taxing and holding back the rich, the able, the hard-working, and allowing the weak, the unable, the inefficient to survive, and therefore multiply without improvement.

Under the banner of "root, hog, or die," the famed Yale economist W. G. Sumner argued that nature eliminates inefficiency, and that any interference in this process was doomed to failure. It would backfire on people. The danger of social intervention: Public welfare programs, public health programs, even the most basic public health programs, simply would interfere with the natural processes, and evolution would not be allowed to proceed. In the long run, they would fail, and actually do more than fail. They would actually backfire.

Such Gilded Age industrialists such as Andrew Carnegie, John D. Rockefeller, and James J. Hill publicly and very bluntly justified their cutthroat business practices in social Darwinist terms. They said that what they were doing was right, and this was why it was right. Sure, there were some losers in these business practices, and then there were the winners, of course. They happened to be the winners, and it was because they were the most fit. Ultimately, it was not to their benefit; ultimately, it was to the benefit of society.

Opponents of public health and welfare programs drew on social Darwinist thinking in shaping American and European public policies throughout the late 1800s, and into the early 1900s.

Biological Darwinists, that is, biologists who espoused Darwinism, did not necessarily accept social Darwinism. A great example of an opponent of social Darwinism among evolutionary biologists was Alfred Russel Wallace. He was a prime advocate of socialism throughout his life, up until his death in the early 1900s. He led a very long life. He was a very active writer, and there was probably no more visible opponent of social Darwinism in all of England than Alfred Russel Wallace. He was constantly publishing arguments attacking it. He argued that humans could guide their own evolution, and were not bound by this biological process. At the time, however, he was swimming upstream.

Social Darwinists continually used biological Darwinism to justify their views, and to give them weight and authority, despite the writings of people like Wallace. For many late 19th-century Europeans and Americans, the most important area of competition was not this competition among workers and manufacturers within society. That was important, but for a lot of them, the most important competition was between different races of humans, and among nations.

Social Darwinism at this time was invoked to justify Western imperialism, colonialism, militarism, and scientific racism. If you think back in history, to what was happening during this time, it was just the time when Europe was pushing out and colonizing Africa, Asia, different places in the world, where militarism picked up. The forms of these views on imperialism, colonialism and the like used social Darwinism to publicly justify their thinking. Let's look at a couple of those.

Think of racism. Of course, racism predated Darwinism. Racism has been, to my knowledge, with humans since the beginning of time. Biological evolution, however, in the late 1800s, appeared to justify racism. They called it "scientific racism," not the benighted racism of the old days. No, scientific racism was going to move ahead the understanding of how race works.

We can see it coming from different sources. Lamarckianism, for example, had posited a hierarchical view of progressive development. We have been talking about that in many of the earlier lectures. It was visualized by some racist biologists at the time that the more "civilized" races, as they called them, were simply further along in evolutionary development than the less civilized races. That is, the cultural development (these were mostly Western Europeans talking) simply expressed this cultural progress, this cultural development, cultural advance, expressed a basic biological difference, biological advance over, for instance, the aborigines of Australia, or the peoples of the Asian subcontinent, or Africa, or different places. This reflected a biological basis, not simply a cultural process.

You could see that among Darwinists of the day, too, not just Lamarckians. Lamarckianism was linear. Darwinism was not the same way; that would have been a kind of branching out with lots of different evolutions that fit the environment. Whatever evolved in Asia, for instance, should benefit that environment; whatever evolved in Africa or Northern Europe should benefit that environment. It is not necessarily hierarchical. That is how we think of Darwinism today. Many people differentiate Lamarckianism from Darwinism—Lamarckianism is hierarchical, and Darwinism isn't—but that isn't how most Darwinists thought back then, including Darwin.

They somehow saw a single line of human development, despite the fact that they should have thought otherwise, and they inevitably viewed Northern Europeans as further along in that development. Explaining this further development, as Darwin and many of them would, they might say, "Well, Northern Europe has a harsher environment, a more hostile environment. That has forced them to develop their brains further, to live in this colder environment, and so there was an environmental, long-term, and then biological, because it was inherited, basis for the superiority of the European race." One would read or hear this commonly, in the writings of the time.

Both the Lamarckian in the late 1800s, and the Darwinian versions of these views inevitably blurred notions of cultural and biological evolution.

Darwin and Spencer believed that racial struggle contributed to human evolution by "superior" races replacing "inferior" ones. Indeed, think of it. Darwin subtitled his 1859 book, *"or the*

Preservation of Favored Races in the Struggle for Life." No one could have read that at all without thinking of human races. It doesn't apply just to human races, but any reader could see that.

This is a classic application of biological thinking to social thinking. At the time, such views seemed to justify the European colonization of Asia and Africa as something that was for the good of those people living there. It also, amazingly, led many European Americans at that time, at the turn of the century, to literally believe that native Americans and African Americans would simply die out in the United States, and that the European American races would just naturally survive and dominate.

Those are some racist applications of Darwinism that were very prominent around the turn of the last century, around 1900. To some, social Darwinism meant military competition among nations. This was also visible at the time.

Beginning in the late 1800s, Germany's leading Darwinist biologist, Ernst Haeckel, argued that nations and races advanced through competition. An ardent nationalist, he advocated a strong, united Germany. At that time, Germany was broken into a lot of different kingdoms and principalities. He said that Germany should all unite together to dominate the world. Haeckel's social Darwinism contributed to the German militarism that led directly up to the First World War. Studies and interviews conducted of military leaders in Germany during the First World War inevitably justified what they were doing in the First World War on Darwinian terms borrowed directly from the writings of people like Ernst Haeckel.

Germany's defeat in that war deeply embittered Haeckel and his followers. Convinced of the biological superiority of the German people, some of Haeckel's followers contributed to the rise of Nazism. His philosophy fit right into Hitler's arguments and teachings, and his policies of racial purity.

Let me give another example of the implications and impact that this Darwinian thinking actually had on social policies. Probably none is more stark than the world of eugenics. Combining Mendelian theories of genetics with social Darwinism led to the worldwide eugenics movement.

Shortly after Darwin published his great book, *Origin of Species*, his cousin, Francis Galton, conceived of the idea to apply its teachings to human development. Let me just read a little passage from Galton. It kind of gives a flavor of what he was doing. I'll give you his description of this, and that I will kind of analyze it, because it had such an impact on social policies of the time. He wrote:

> "It is a first step with farmers and gardeners to endeavor to obtain good breeds of domestic animals, and seditiously to cultivate plants, for it pays them well to do so. If serious inquiries into heredity now know that qualities gained by good nourishment and good education never descend by inheritance, but perish with the individual, whilst inborn qualities are transmitted…"

Social benefits don't make any difference in plants and animals. Environmental improvements live just with that individual. No, it is only the inborn qualities that are transmitted. He goes on to write:

> "…it is therefore a waste of labor to try to improve a poor stock by careful feeding, or careful gardening."

Think of the application for taking care of "inferior" people. He goes on to write:

> "The question was then forced upon me. Could not the race of man be similarly improved? Could not the undesirables be gotten rid of, and the desirables multiplied? The answer to these questions was a decided 'yes,' and in this way, I lighted on what is now known as eugenics."

As another species, Galton argued, fit humans produce fit offspring, and unfit humans produce unfit offspring. As a thinking species, humans can use this to accelerate the evolutionary process through the selective breeding of humans, just as they do the selective breeding of cows or plants.

Galton defended his theory with social surveys and polls that purportedly showed that ability and success ran in families, while inability and failure ran in other families.

Of course, this could have just as easily been explained by the environments of those families—that environmentally favored families produce environmentally favored offspring. That's just not the way Galton, Darwin's cousin, saw it. He thought, instead, that it showed that there was an inherited goodness, and an inherited badness running through these families.

He was blatant about it. He linked intelligence, beauty, and health with ability. Intelligence would show ability, beauty would show ability, health would show ability, and they all would be together. Ignorance, ugliness, and sickness were connected with inability. In fact, in a popular British journal, he once published a beauty map of England, where the most beautiful women of England were found, so that males seeking a eugenic mate would know where to go—I suppose to pick up the most beautiful mate, who would therefore also be the most intelligent, the most able, the most eugenically fit.

In 1883, Galton actually coined the term "eugenics." He had been writing about it for about a decade before that, to designate policies and programs designed to encourage more children from the fit, and fewer children from the unfit.

Eugenics was sort of a cult idea for half a generation, but it gained widespread interest after the 1900 rediscovery of Mendelian genetics, which made it all seem more credible. Certainly, there were followers before that, but it was Mendelian genetics, when combined with evolutionary thought, that made it pop over the top as accepted social policy.

Genetics appeared to offer a physical basis for Galton's theories. Many experts saw such traits as mental illness, mental retardation, epilepsy, gross physical defects, and criminality as the products of easily eliminated, simple, hereditary factors, much like tall pea plants and short pea plants; criminals, non-criminals. If you want tall pea plants, you pick the tall pea plants as the parents. If you want to get rid of criminals, just get rid of the gene that causes criminality. This was widespread thought at the time.

This, of course, was a time when science was held in high esteem, when biology was coming into its own, when genetics seemed to offer new solutions. Here, eugenics appeared to offer a scientific methodology for social sciences. "Nature" all but replaced "nurture" within social scientific thinking.

The IQ was invented at this time as an objective measure of intelligence. Before that, I suppose people thought that there were people who were smarter, and people who were not as smart, but they wanted to quantify this to use it in eugenics. They came up with the idea that you could quantify intelligence through IQ, and having IQ tests. The IQ test was actually brought to America to be used to differentiate people by eugenicists who wanted to use it to categorize people, and decide who should be encouraged to breed, and who should be discouraged from breeding.

Sociologists at this time conducted public health surveys, and compiled family pedigrees to show a hereditary basis for crime, poverty, antisocial behavior, and low IQ. Since they went looking for those things, they found plenty of survey evidence, because who they picked and how they picked seemed to support their ideas.

Although eugenics never really gained broad popular appeal among the masses in America, many scientific, professional, and philanthropic organizations promoted its acceptance actively. These efforts greatly influenced public policies throughout the United States and Europe during the first quarter or first third of the 20th century.

They basically formed into two types. There was one variety of public policies and programs that would go under the rubric of "positive" eugenics. These theories and approaches sought more children from the fit. We can see it in an amazing variety of people. People don't talk about this anymore, because we remember the other aspects of some of these great leaders. You can look at many of the great leaders of the time, however. Winston Churchill was once a prime proponent of positive eugenics in England. Teddy Roosevelt in America, as well as Woodrow Wilson, Calvin Coolidge, many of our early presidents during this time in the early 20th century were strong proponents of eugenic thinking in public policies. They worried that the professional classes were not reproducing in sufficient numbers. Women weren't having enough babies; people were moving into professional families, and weren't having enough children.

Progressive sociologist and good friend of Teddy Roosevelt, Edward A. Ross, called it "race suicide." It crept into Teddy Roosevelt's speech that "race suicide" was going on, because the able women were now going to college, and were not producing enough kids. Professional families were not having enough children, as they had in the past. They were going to be swamped by the inferior products of their own race, as the term would come out. "Lower" classes of whites would keep producing; working families of these "better" families would not produce enough.

Education efforts taught students the value of eugenic mate selection. You can look at the biology and civics textbooks of the time and see eugenic mating advice, and the importance of having large families. Organizations, even county fairs, would hold "fitter family" contests and "eugenic baby" contests, much like they would give prizes for the best sheep at a 4-H contest, to the best family, the biggest eugenic family, producing the "best" children, the most kids—ways to propagate production by the "fit."

Eugenic fitness was proposed as a prerequisite for marriage. Many states adopted laws requiring a eugenic test before a person could get married. Some churches, such as the Episcopal Church, actively proposed ideas that only eugenically fit people could be married in a proper church wedding. Some countries adopted tax and employment policies to encourage its "able" citizens to have children.

That was positive eugenics. There was also "negative eugenics," the other side, the dark side of eugenics, as it were, that sought fewer children from the "unfit." Every single American state and most Western countries adopted policies during this period of sexually segregating certain supposedly dysgenic classes, typically the mentally retarded, during their breeding years, so that they could not reproduce.

Thirty-five American states, and many European countries, instituted compulsory programs of sexual sterilization for the mentally ill and retarded, for habitual criminals, for epileptics. Germany's programs, which were adopted during the Weimar Republic, were later extended under the Nazi era to include Jews, gypsies, and other disfavored groups.

During the period from 1900–1960, some 60,000 Americans were sterilized under compulsory state programs, and many more were sterilized under voluntary programs, such as when people were brought in by their parents for sterilization because of some supposed eugenic defect. Such programs were even upheld as constitutional by the United States Supreme Court in 1927, in a case involving Carrie Buck, a woman at a Virginia mental institution who was sterilized against her will under evidence that both her mother and grandmother had been mentally retarded. It was claimed that she was mentally retarded, but she really wasn't. Oliver Wendell Holmes, Jr. wrote a decision for a nearly unanimous Supreme Court that said that this sacrifice was appropriate for society because, as he put it, "Three generations of imbeciles are enough."

Partly on eugenics grounds, Congress passed laws curtailing the immigration of non-Nordic stock that were seen as inappropriate for North America. Nazi Germany moved from eugenic sterilization to euthanasia, and German geneticists joined in supporting these racial purity policies. We can go back and look. Biologists joined the Nazi party at a higher rate than other professional groups. Except for the Catholic Church, opposition to eugenics was disorganized and ineffective until the 1930s, when Nazi practices discredited the lot.

Then, gradually, social scientists and later geneticists began turning from these ideas as too simplistic to explain complicated, multi-factorial traits and abilities of people. By the end of World War II, social Darwinism was morally bankrupt, but for a period of a half-century, it had profoundly influenced how scientifically informed governments treated their most vulnerable citizens.

Lecture Nine
America's Anti-Evolution Crusade

Scope:

Decades of popular concern over the theory of evolution erupted during the 1920s into a crusade by conservative American Protestants against teaching evolution in public schools. The crusade was part of their larger effort to defend traditional beliefs and values against liberalism in the church and secularism in society. Crusaders met immediate opposition from religious liberals and a broad array of secularists. The battle was joined over the theory of evolution because both sides viewed it as central to religious liberalism and scientific secularism.

The battle reached its public climax in 1925, when Tennessee's new law against teaching evolution was challenged by a schoolteacher named John Scopes. The nation watched as Christian politician William Jennings Bryan and agnostic lawyer Clarence Darrow dueled over the anti-evolution law in court. They helped make the issue into a flashpoint for public controversy.

Outline

I. Conservative Christians had never liked the Darwinian theory of human evolution. Their long-simmering concern boiled over during the 1920s into a crusade against teaching it in public schools.

   A. Several factors contributed to the timing of America's anti-evolution crusade.

   1. Protestant fundamentalism had increased in reaction to religious liberalism in the major mainline Protestant denominations. Conservatives saw an evolutionary view of religion at the heart of the liberal heresy.

   2. Darwinism was being revived in evolutionary science because of greater understanding of genetics.

   3. Compulsory high school education was becoming commonplace; evolutionary teaching reached more students and families.

   4. Evolutionary thinking was associated in the public mind with German militarism, laissez-faire capitalism, and eugenics.

5. The 1920s were a period of heightened social stress as reform and reaction competed for America's future. The Jazz Age battled with the "return to normalcy."

B. Around 1920, several fundamentalist leaders began targeting the theory of evolution for public condemnation.

1. Leading the attacks were three Baptist ministers, William Bell Riley of Minneapolis, John Roach Straton of New York City, and J. Frank Norris of Dallas. Institutional centers of anti-evolutionism were the World's Christian Fundamentals Association, Chicago's Moody Bible Institute, and the Bible Institute of Los Angeles.

2. Mainline Protestant denominations became embroiled in bitter doctrinal disputes over teaching evolution in church colleges and from the pulpit. Conservatives demanded orthodoxy with respect to the special creation of humans in God's image.

3. Conservative Protestant denominations and independent Bible churches and schools reemphasized a literalistic interpretation of Genesis as foundational.

C. Religious liberals fought back in defense of modern science and an evolutionary view of religious understanding.

1. Leading the defense were University of Chicago theologian Shailer Mathews and New York Baptist/Presbyterian minister Harry Emerson Fosdick. Most of the mainline Protestant denominations ultimately sided with the liberals.

2. Leading scientists and political figures with religious affiliations, such as Henry Fairfield Osborn, Robert Millikan, and Herbert Hoover, denounced anti-evolutionism.

II. In 1922, William Jennings Bryan transformed this religious dispute into a political battle.

A. At age 62, Bryan was a living legend.

1. He had been nominated for president by the Democratic Party at age 36, the youngest presidential nominee of any major political party, and re-nominated twice more. The Populist Party also nominated him for president once.

2. Following his defeats, he remained in the public eye as a speaker and writer for progressive political causes and served as Woodrow Wilson's secretary of state until he resigned that post in protest of Wilson's drift toward entry in World War I.

3. His progressive politics and anti-militarism always had a moralistic religious tint, which became more pronounced over time. By the 1920s, he had become a leader of fundamentalist forces in the Presbyterian Church.

B. In 1921, Bryan heard of an attempt by Kentucky Baptists to politicize the anti-evolution movement by seeking legislation to outlaw the teaching of Darwinism in public schools.

1. As a political progressive, Bryan welcomed legislative solutions to social problems.

2. As a conservative Protestant, Bryan deplored Darwinism as corrosive of religion.

3. As a left-leaning politician, he opposed social Darwinism, eugenics, militarism, imperialism, and laissez-faire capitalism.

4. As a rural populist from Nebraska, he was suspicious of elite institutions, such as science, and believed that the people had a right to control public education.

5. In 1922, he went to Kentucky in support of the Baptist measure to outlaw the teaching of evolution, then carried his crusade for such laws nationwide.

C. Bryan objected only to teaching the Darwinian theory of human evolution. He viewed the days of creation as symbolic of geological ages and acknowledged that "lower" animals may have evolved.

1. Bryan's concern always focused on people and what a belief in a "brute ancestry" might mean for human morality and religious faith.

2. After several near misses and a few partial victories for Bryan's crusade, in 1925, Tennessee became the first state to outlaw the teaching of human evolution in public schools. It was a misdemeanor subject to a fine of up to $500.

3. The law exceeded Bryan's proposal by covering all theories of human evolution, not just Darwinism, and imposing a criminal penalty. The Tennessee governor

still viewed it as a symbolic measure, not an enforceable statute.

4. It gained immediate notoriety, with religious conservatives hailing it and most others scorning it. No one expected that teachers would be prosecuted under it.

III. The initial attention attracted by the new Tennessee statute expanded into a media frenzy when, six weeks after it became law, John Scopes was indicted for violating it.

A. From its bizarre beginnings to its inconclusive outcome, the Scopes trial was never a normal criminal prosecution.

1. Soon after Tennessee enacted its anti-evolution statute, the ACLU offered to defend any Tennessee schoolteacher willing to challenge the law's constitutionality in court.

2. Dayton civic leaders invited local science teacher John Scopes to accept the ACLU offer as a means to publicize their town. Scopes agreed to the scheme even though he was not a biology teacher and had never violated the statute.

3. Scopes's indictment made front-page news around the world. He was never arrested nor threatened with jail and spent much of the time until trial in media appearances.

B. Both sides in the larger controversy saw the pending trial as an opportunity to make their case to the public. It became a show trial for all concerned.

1. America's most famous trial lawyer and religious skeptic, Clarence Darrow, led a team of crack ACLU lawyers to Dayton to defend Scopes. Their stated goal was to debunk religious lawmaking and promote individual freedom.

2. Bryan joined the prosecution in an effort to articulate the case against teaching evolution and defend the right of a popular majority to control public education. He knew that the law (not Scopes) was actually on trial.

3. The media promoted this heavyweight bout as "the trial of the century" before it even began. It was broadcast over the radio, filmed for newsreels, and covered by more than 200 reporters from the United States and Europe.

C. The eight-day trial was largely anticlimactic as each side made its familiar arguments. Neither side disputed that Scopes had violated the law, and the court foreclosed other issues as irrelevant to the case.

1. When the judge refused to strike the statute as unconstitutional, the defense all but asked the jury to convict Scopes so that they could appeal the judge's ruling to a higher court. The jury did so, and Scopes was fined $100.

2. The trial's most memorable event was when Darrow invited Bryan to take the stand as a witness in defense of the anti-evolution statute. Darrow asked questions about biblical literalism that made Bryan and the Genesis account look foolish.

3. Following his conviction, Scopes was offered his job back but instead accepted a scholarship to study geology at the University of Chicago. He became a petroleum engineer in Venezuela and later managed an oil refinery in Louisiana.

4. Bryan died in Dayton less than a week after the trial, but his crusade continued.

5. Scopes's conviction was overturned on appeal, but the anti-evolution statute was upheld as constitutional. Other states and school districts imposed similar measures.

D. The trial left a bitter legacy of deep division over the teaching of evolution in public school. Each side had persuaded its followers of the critical importance of the issue.

Essential Reading:

Larson, *Summer for the Gods.*

Supplementary Reading:

Conkin, *When All the Gods Trembled.*

Numbers, *Darwinism Comes to America*, ch. 4.

Questions to Consider:

1. Why did a massive popular crusade against the teaching of human evolution in public schools erupt in the United States some 60 years after Darwin published his theory? What were the main points of contention?

2. How did a misdemeanor case in a small Tennessee town become America's "trial of the century"? Was all the media and public attention on it justified? What was the trial's lasting impact on the creation-evolution controversy?

Lecture Nine—Transcript
America's Anti-Evolution Crusade

Hello, and welcome back. In the last lecture, we were talking about social Darwinism. Throughout this whole course, we have been talking about evolutionary science. Social Darwinism and evolutionary science produced a popular backlash in America, in the 1920s. It was known as America's anti-evolution crusade. That is what I want to talk about today.

As we've seen, conservative Christians have never liked the Darwinian theory of human evolution. Their long-simmering concern boiled over during in the 1920s into a crusade against teaching that theory in public schools.

Several factors contributed to the timing of America's anti-evolution crusade. These are important to follow, because people often ask me why, so many years after the publication of *Origin of Species*, a crusade began to boil up in the 1920s, of all times. Why didn't it happen earlier? Why didn't it happen in the 1860s?

There are several factors that contributed to this. Let me go over at least five of them that seem to stand out in my mind. Certainly any historical event has quite a bit of causation. No historian can analyze it all, but five seem to stand out in my mind.

The first of these is perhaps the most complex and the most difficult for people today to understand, because naturally, people are present-minded, and we have a view that things are developing over time, is the evolutionary worldview that most of us have. Protestant fundamentalism, however, actually had increased within the mainline religious denominations during the years leading up to the 1920s. It wasn't decreasing. Indeed, the term " fundamentalism" that is now so common was originally coined only around 1920 to characterize a group of religious believers within the mainline Protestant denominations.

If you go back in time to the 1800s, you'll find that, sure, American Protestants were divided into their different denominations, such as Methodists or Baptists, Presbyterians and Episcopalians. For the most part, however, those denominations pretty well hung together. There were tensions within the denominations, but basically they were kept within the group.

What happened in the late 1800s was that there was a rise of religious liberalism in the mainline denominations, especially the Methodists, Presbyterians, Episcopalians, where notions of higher criticism of the Bible—that is, treating the Bible as a " written work" by people, new, critical, textual analysis of the Bible, and a view of the evolutionary development coming out of science applied to religion—and the notion that the Bible, while everyone within these denominations, the theologians, viewed the Bible as a special work, it was viewed as the work of a people, beginning with the Hebrew people, and their view of God.

They had one view of God early on, but as they developed as a civilization, they had an increasingly sophisticated view of God. The early books of the Bible were, by the liberals, viewed as a fair view of the way that the early Hebrew people viewed God. Then, there was the later Old Testament, so that you had the prophetic books, which were more enriched, and then the New Testament, a sort of fuller view of God—a more civilized view, a more enriched view. This was an evolutionary view of religion.

Against this, conservatives within the church fought back, because they held a very high view of scripture. To them, the entire scripture was the word of God. Certainly, the liberals would say this too, but they meant that it was inspired in a special way, and that it was the people's understanding of God. It was very, very important, but was not the literal word of God.

Conservatives saw this evolutionary view of religion that liberals were positing as the heart of what was really a modernist heresy; it was undercutting a very high view of scripture, while the conservatives saw the whole Bible as equally important. This was a change, and those conservatives, beginning about 1920, were called "fundamentalists." It was known as the " fundamentalist modernist controversy" that was tearing apart the mainline religious denominations, the Methodists, Episcopals, Presbyterians, and Baptists. It really came to the point where the fundamentalists within those different denominations, now perhaps called " evangelicals," had more in common with each other than they did with the liberals within their own denominations. The liberals within those denominations had more in common across denominations. American Protestantism was splitting open under not the denominational divisions, but modernist fundamentalist denominations. This was important background for what we are going to be talking about.

Further, there were other factors that are easier and quicker to explain. Darwinism, as we've seen, was beginning to revive within evolutionary science, with the advent of a greater understanding of genetics; that is, pure, classical Darwinism. That was more hostile to a religious view than neo-Lamarckianism, or orthogenesis, or certainly, theistic evolution.

Third, compulsory high school education was just beginning to take effect around the country at this time. This was pushing evolutionary teaching into the faces of more parents. Before that, people only mostly went to elementary school, where, of course, evolution isn't taught. That is a high school subject. With more people forced to go to school, more children going to school, more parents who were suspicious of evolution for religious reasons were now having it enforced on their children, and they were reacting.

Fourth, evolutionary thinking at this time was associated in the public mind with German militarism; remember that World War I had just finished, with laissez-faire capitalism, with all of the struggles of labor against capital, and with eugenics, which was in its heyday in the 1920s. This gave a negative view of evolution for many people.

Finally, the 1920s themselves were a period of heightened social stress as reform competed with reaction for America's future. Think of it: The Jazz Age battled with the "return to normalcy."

With this background, in 1920 several fundamentalist leaders began targeting the theory of evolution for public condemnation. If we go back much before 1920, fundamentalists, or conservative Christians, just didn't say too much about it. Now, however, they saw this as a hot button issue to arouse their followers, who were concerned mostly about an evolutionary view of religion.

Leading the attack were three Baptists ministers. Two of them were American Baptists, one of whom was William Bell Riley of Minneapolis, the other John Roach Straton of New York. One was Southern Baptist J. Frank Norris of Dallas. The institutional centers of the anti-evolution crusade were some large, newly formed, fundamentalist, conservative institutions that attracted widespread followings across the denominations. Before this time, there were

©2002 The Teaching Company Limited Partnership

mostly denominational institutions. Now there were interdenominational institutions that united the conservatives, versus those that united the liberals or the modernists. This group was the World's Christian Fundamentals Association, a predecessor of today's National Association of Evangelicals; Chicago's Moody Bible Institute; and the Bible Institute of Los Angeles, now known as Biola.

Mainline Protestant denominations became embroiled in bitter disputes over the teaching of evolution, particularly an evolutionary view of religion within church colleges, such as Baylor, and from the pulpit, with ministers teaching this particular view of religion, or this particular view of origins, because the evolutionary view of religion ultimately got tied up in the evolutionary view of biology. Whether those things were taught from the pulpit or in church colleges became a major issue.

Conservatives demanded orthodoxy with respect to the special creation of humans in God's image. Conservative Protestant denominations and independent Bible churches, as well as freestanding Christian schools like Wheaton College, reemphasized the literal interpretation of Genesis as foundational. This was key not only because it was Genesis, but because it reflected the position that proponents were holding to the whole Bible: "The whole Bible must be believed as true, and we are not going to allow the Old Testament to be just dismissed as an early, crude vision of early peoples, and early civilizations and their view of God. We are standing with the whole Bible as inerrant, and directly inspired by God."

On the other side, the religious liberals fought back with the defense of modern science and an evolutionary view of religious understanding. Leading the defense, most visible in the public mind, were the University of Chicago theologian Schailer Mathews and New York's nationally famous Presbyterian-turned-Baptist minister, Harry Emerson Fosdick. Most of the mainline Protestant denominations were rent by this division, with great debate in their conventions year after year, from about 1920 to 1930.

In most of the mainline denominations, the liberals ultimately won out, or the modernists won out. Certainly that was true of the American Baptists, the Methodists, and Presbyterian and Episcopal churches of this time. Perhaps only the Southern Baptists leaned more toward the conservative side.

Leading scientists and political figures who were deeply religious themselves, most of them modernists or liberals, got involved in this debate and took it to the public. It was probably best known in the world of science: Henry Fairfield Osborn was a very visible paleontologist who led the American Museum of Natural History, and Robert Millikan, America's Nobel laureate at Caltech. In addition, Herbert Hoover, who was a great engineer-turned-politician, and famous for his war relief work in World War I. These were visible opponents who would denounce anti-evolutionism.

In 1924, William Jennings Bryan transformed this essentially religious dispute within the churches of American Protestantism into a major political battle and political crusade. At age 62, William Jennings Bryan was living legend, and America's most famous orator. He had been nominated for president by the Democratic Party at age 36, the youngest major party presidential candidate nominee of any major political party ever. He had then been re-nominated twice more. The Populist Party had also nominated him once for president.

Following his defeats, and he was narrowly defeated in each case, he remained in the public eye as a speaker and writer for progressive political causes. He served as Woodrow Wilson's Secretary of State until he resigned that post in protest over Wilson's drift toward World War I. Bryan was always an anti-militarist, almost a pacifist.

His progressive politics and his anti-militarism always had a moralistic, religious tint to it, which became more pronounced over time. Think of him today as something like Jimmy Carter. By the 1920s, he led the fundamentalist or conservative forces within the mainline Northern Presbyterian Church.

In 1921, Bryan heard of an attempt by Kentucky Baptists to politicize the anti-evolution movement—a movement that, remember, had been mostly within the church—by seeking legislation by state law, in the state of Kentucky, to outlaw the teaching of Darwinism in public schools, bringing in this concern about what was taught to children from a battle within the church. With children going off to school and hearing that Darwinism was true, reinforcing the other side in this religious dispute, they argued that this should not be taught in public schools.

As a political progressive, Bryan instinctively welcomed legislative solutions to, or legislative ways to deal with, social problems. As a political conservative, Bryan deplored Darwinism as corrosive of religion. As a left-leaning politician, he opposed social Darwinism, eugenics, militarism, imperialism, and laissez-faire capitalism. As a rural populist from Nebraska, he was suspicious of elite institutions, such as science. He believed that the people had a right to control public education, so he saw this Kentucky proposal as a natural, a political, legislative solution to what he perceived as an important social religious problem. In 1922, Bryan went to Kentucky to support the Baptist measure to outlaw the teaching of evolution, and then carried his crusade for such laws nationwide.

Kentucky turned out to be a narrow defeat. It was strongly opposed by the president of the state university there, and lost by one vote in the legislature. Of course, Bryan was used to losing, and he was used to battling for causes. He was very involved in a whole series of campaigns that initially lost, such as female suffrage, which he was greatly responsible for getting the states to eventually pass. He fought for that for years. Of course, he fought against militarism, and was used to defeat there, with the coming of World War I. He fought against capitalism and large business industry; he wanted regulation of industry, and regulation of business. Those were long-fought battles. He was used to fighting hard, and he was a natural campaigner.

During his entire political and public speaking career, he gave an average of 200 addresses a year. He was always on the road speaking. What happened after his narrow defeat in Kentucky in 1922 was that he took on the road, along with his crusades for other things, a crusade for anti-evolution. He took it around the country to state after state. In state after state, these issues started coming up and being debated in state legislatures.

If you look back at his speeches, you can see that Bryan took a very focused line. He objected only to the teaching of the Darwinian theory of human evolution. He actually viewed the days of creation as symbolic of vast geological ages. He totally bought into the view that the world was very old. He also acknowledged that "lower forms" of animals, as he called them, that is, plants and animals other than humans, may well have evolved over time.

His concern always focused on people. His political concerns always focused on taking care of the common person. In this case, what he was concerned about was the belief that a "brute ancestry" of humans, as he called it—that humans were descended from apes— what that might mean: that it might undercut human morality; might undercut religious faith. It was important that humans believe they were special; he believed they were special, and divinely created in God's image.

The crusade went on for several years. After several near-misses, and a few partial victories in states like Florida and Oklahoma, in 1925, Tennessee became the first state in the union to outlaw the teaching of human evolution in public schools. Under the new Tennessee law, it was a misdemeanor punishable by a maximum fine of up to $500—$100 to $500. The law itself exceeded Bryan's proposal, because it covered all theories of human evolution, not just Darwinism, which was the only one he was concerned about. He was not particularly concerned about theistic evolution or some other versions.

It also imposed a criminal penalty that he did not want, because he thought it would just create martyrs of the teachers. He just wanted to make it against the law. Despite these additions, the governor of Tennessee signed it; he viewed it as a symbolic measure that would not be an enforceable statute.

Nevertheless, coming as it did after a long public division over evolution within American religion, that had given the whole issue major attention and major press for five years, at the heels of a three-year long speaking campaign by Bryan, which had stirred up legislative efforts in dozens of states around the country, this was a nationally noted event. This wasn't just some weird activity off in some borderland state. This was viewed nationally as an important event. This was front page news around the country that Tennessee had finally passed such a law, given the background. It stirred up major attention, with religious conservatives backing it, but with most other people who were sensitized to this issue, such as President Calvin Coolidge, Herbert Hoover, and Robert Millikan, denouncing this, scorning it. However, no one expected that any teacher would ever be prosecuted under it.

The initial attention attracted by the new Tennessee statute expanded into a virtual media frenzy, when, six weeks after the statute became law, John Scopes was indicted for violating it. From its bizarre beginnings, to its inconclusive end, the " Scopes trial," as it ultimately became known, was never a normal criminal prosecution. Let's go over a little bit of the background of what led to it.

Soon after Tennessee enacted its anti-evolution statute, the ACLU from New York offered, in a press release, to defend any Tennessee schoolteacher willing to challenge this law's constitutionality in court, in a test case of some sort.

Dayton's civic leaders (Dayton was then a small town in east Tennessee, and was in a bit of economic crisis because its main industry had closed recently) invited a local science teacher named John Scopes to accept the ACLU challenge as a means to publicize their town. Apparently, back then, any sort of publicity was welcome.

Scopes agreed to the scheme, even though he was not a biology teacher, and he had never actually violated the statute. Scopes's indictment made front page news around the world. He was never arrested. Indeed, he was never even threatened with jail. He was assured of his job back the following year, because he had been invited to challenge the case by the president of the school board and his own superintendent of schools, with the avid backing of the principal and everyone else involved in town. Actually, he spent most of the time between his indictment and the actual trial making media appearances, traveling to New York and Washington, D.C.

Both sides in the larger controversy saw the pending trial as an opportunity to make their case to the general public. Both Bryan and the ACLU lawyers recognized this opportunity as one to make their case. Modernists, liberals, fundamentalists, and conservatives saw this as their chance. They knew the world would be watching.

It became a show trial for all concerned. During the actual trial, John Scopes virtually disappeared. He never testified at trial, never made a major appearance. The trial was turned over to the protagonists, the lawyers on both sides who would argue the case.

On the defense side, America's most famous trial lawyer and a noted religious skeptic, who was known throughout the country for giving speeches and writing books about the dangers of religious lawmaking, and the dangers of a literalistic belief in the Bible and of revealed religion, was a man named Clarence Darrow, and at the time, he was a very visible, highly paid, very respected criminal lawyer. He volunteered his services, and went along to lead a dedicated team of crack ACLU lawyers to Dayton, to defend Scopes. It was the only time in Clarence Darrow's entire career that he volunteered his legal services. At the time, he was charging up to a quarter of a million dollars a case to defend people.

His goal, and indeed, the goal of the entire ACLU team, was to debunk religious lawmaking as improper, and to say that the Bible was not a fit standard to determine educational policies in a school. The ACLU team and Clarence Darrow also wanted to promote individual liberty, the freedom of individual teachers to teach what they thought was good science, as well as academic freedom, the individual freedom of parents and teachers not to be imposed upon with religious instruction.

On the other side, while the defense team was assembled to attack the statute, and was clearly planning to use the trial as a vehicle to promote their views, William Jennings Bryan, who was a lawyer himself, but had not practiced law in over 30 years, volunteered as well, to join the prosecution, along with, of course, the local prosecutors, to make the case against the teaching of evolution, and to defend the right of a popular majority to control public education. He knew that the law, and not John Scopes, was actually on trial.

The media promoted this heavyweight bout as "the trial of the century" before it even began. Yet, think of it. This was just a simple little misdemeanor trial with a potential fine of $500. It wasn't a major murder trial. Indeed, one of things I so like about this trial is that has at least partially lived up to its billing as the trial of the century. We think of the great trials of America as these great murder trials, where there was some awful murder involved. This, however, was a trial over an idea. Scopes was not really on trial; it was the idea of evolutionary teaching, the ideal of academic freedom, and the ideal of popular control over education. To me, as an intellectual historian, it is sort of nice that this could be the trial of the century.

It was promoted heavily by the media, as I said, even before it began. It was broadcast over the radio. It was the first broadcast trial in American history. It was filmed for newsreel footages right in the courtroom, and the footage was flown out every day, shown in movie halls in the north, and eventually, all over the country, so that people could actually watch the trial. It was covered by over 200 reporters from the United States and Europe. The courtroom was cleared out so that the reporters had the central section. Telegraph wires were laid right into the courtroom so that they could report out their stories. The transcript, and every word spoken was telegraphed out to different media outlets around the country. It was an amazing event. Indeed, it was reported at the end that more words had been telegraphed from the United States to England about this trial than at any other event that had previously occurred in American history.

The eight-day trial itself was largely anticlimactic, as each side made its by now very familiar argument. These had been circling around for four or five years. Neither side disputed that Scopes had violated the law. The court ultimately foreclosed the other issues as irrelevant to that one issue, whether Scopes had violated the law.

When the judge refused strike the statute as unconstitutional, the defense, led by Clarence Darrow, all but asked the jury to convict Scopes so that they could appeal the judge's ruling to a higher court. If Scopes had not been convicted, if the statute had been upheld but it was ruled that Scopes had not violated the law, then there would not have been any appeal; they could not have challenged the law. So, at the end, Darrow actually asked the jury to convict Scopes. They did, and he was fined the minimum amount of a $100 fine, which was paid on his behalf by H. L. Mencken, one of the reporters covering the trial.

The trial's most memorable event occurred near its end. After it appeared to be all but over except for the closing arguments—everyone knew that Darrow and Bryan were there to discuss the larger issues—at the end, Clarence Darrow invited William Jennings Bryan to take the stand as a witness for the defense of the anti-evolution statute. Of course, there was no legal authority to do this. You can't call the opposing counsel and ask them questions. Bryan agreed to do so, however, to defend his statute, which he knew was on trial here.

Rather than asking about the statute, Darrow asked questions about biblical literalism, such as: Did Jonah live inside the whale for three days? Was Eve made by Adam's rib? These kinds of questions.

These were questions about biblical literalism that made Bryan and the Genesis account look foolish.

Following his conviction, Scopes was offered his job back, but instead, he accepted a scholarship to study geology at the University of Chicago. He became a petroleum engineer in Venezuela, and later managed an oil refinery in Louisiana.

Bryan died in Dayton less than the week after the trial, caused partly by the stress of the trial and the oppressive heat in Dayton, but his crusade continued. After Bryan's death, Scopes's conviction went on to appeal in the Tennessee Supreme Court. The Tennessee Supreme Court overturned Scopes's conviction on a technicality, but it upheld the anti-evolution statute as constitutional, which foreclosed any further appeal to the U.S. Supreme Court. Since the statute was upheld as constitutional, and there was pressure for such laws, other states and school districts imposed similar measures. If you look through the textbooks of the time, because of this controversy, the theory of evolution virtually disappeared from most popular high school biology textbooks during the years that followed the Scopes trial.

The trial left a bitter legacy of deep division over the teaching of evolution in public schools. Each side had persuaded its own followers of the critical importance of this issue; that this, the teaching of evolution and the issue of human evolution in particular, was something worth fighting for.

Lecture Ten
The Neo-Darwinian Synthesis

Scope:

By the 1940s, a consensus emerged among biologists on how the evolutionary process worked. It untied the laboratory research of geneticists and the fieldwork of naturalists to rout notions of acquired characteristics, vital forces, and external design from mainstream biology. Evolution, this synthesis maintained, was a purely materialistic process driven by the natural selection of random variation at the genetic level. In these respects, this so-called "modern," or "neo-Darwinian," synthesis was more fully Darwinian than Darwin's own conclusions.

Although this breakthrough was largely conceptual, it found its classic case in David Lack's 1947 interpretation of the evolutionary development of Darwin's finches on the Galapagos Islands. This famous sub-family of birds, which once inspired Darwin, had remained incomprehensible under selection theory. Lack's interpretation, as later developed by Peter and Rosemary Grant and featured in countless biology textbooks and works of popular science, became the best known example of natural selection at work among living organisms.

Outline

I. During the first quarter of the 20th century, scientists remained deeply divided over how evolution operated. None of them saw a significant role for natural selection in the process.

   A. Field naturalists tended to follow Alfred Russel Wallace in stressing the role of geographical isolation and environmental adaptation in evolution but favored Lamarckian mechanisms as the cause of variation.

   B. Paleontologists interpreted the fossil record to show linear evolutionary development over time, as expected under Lamarckism, orthogenesis, or theistic evolution.

C. Geneticists and other laboratory biologists rejected Lamarckism in favor of discontinuous Mendelian mutations feeding evolution with little role for the adaptive value of mutations or the selection of the fittest. This notion worked in laboratories but not in the wild.

II. Aspects of each view merged into a neo-Darwinian synthesis as scientists gained greater understanding of genetic and geographic factors.

A. The first steps toward the neo-Darwinian synthesis were taken during the 1920s, when geneticists began appreciating complexity in the genetics of large populations.

1. Early Mendelians studied discontinuous single-gene traits (e.g., tall or short pea plants), thinking that single-gene mutations gave birth to new species or varieties. They had ignored the seemingly continuous variability of large populations.

2. Increasingly, they now recognized that multiple-gene interactions affect any one trait, such that single-gene changes might cause seemingly continuous variations in that trait. N. Nilsson-Ehle calculated that if 10 genes affected one trait, then the trait might have 60,000 different variations.

3. This view dispensed with a blending view of inheritance for continuous variations and, thus, solved the problem that even beneficial variations would be swamped in reproduction. Minor nonfatal variations could survive in a population, and beneficial ones would spread through natural selection.

4. R.A. Fisher proposed that a large population of any species contains great genetic variability, which allows it to evolve gradually in response to environmental changes. Even harmful genes could survive if recessive and emerge as conditions warranted.

5. J.B.S. Haldane offered the example of the peppered moth, in which the population evolved in 50 years from mostly light-colored varieties to mostly dark-colored ones as increasing industrial soot in Britain gave selective advantage to darkness.

6. Genetic mutations circulate in a population even if they confer no benefit, allowing a species to build a fund of variability to be exploited by selection if conditions change. Gene mutations and recombinations add to variability in a population but do not trigger its evolution.

B. Theories about the evolution of large populations did not interest field naturalists, who saw speciation in the wild occurring mostly in small populations isolated on the fringe of larger populations. During the 1920s, geneticist Sewall Wright addressed this issue.

1. Through laboratory experiments with small populations, Wright found that intense inbreeding produced extreme variability in a species.

2. He showed mathematically that inbreeding could drive a small, isolated population to deviate from the parent population. If the deviation proved beneficial in the isolated locale, natural selection could generate rapid evolution.

3. In 1937, Theodosius Dobzhansky applied Wright's theory to wild populations to find that, given the reservoir of variability in a population, natural selection could cause gradual evolution under changed conditions and stability under constant conditions.

4. By the early 1940s, the influential British science writer Julian Huxley brought together these various insights from genetics and evolutionary biology into what he termed the "modern synthesis."

C. Led by Ernst Mayr in 1942, field naturalists agreed that the new genetics could explain the evolution of isolated populations without the need for invoking Lamarckism.

1. They stressed that speciation occurs only through an initial phase of geographic isolation. Without crossbreeding, each population could develop such separate traits that they could or would no longer crossbreed when brought back together.

2. These reproductively isolated variations, sub-species, or related species would have evolved to fit their separate environments in a process called "adaptive radiation."

3. If reunited with kindred types, competition would drive them even further apart.

4. Mayr concluded, "A new species develops if a population which has become geographically isolated from its parental species acquires during this period of isolation characters which promote or guarantee reproductive isolation when the external barriers break down."

5. Seen in this way, a species becomes a range of gene frequencies in a reproductively isolated population, not an ideally created archetype. Evolution occurs whenever the range shifts. It is a purely materialistic chemical process.

D. Led by George Gaylord Simpson in 1944, paleontologists concluded that this neo-Darwinian view of the origin of species did not conflict with the fossil record. Its gaps could be the result of rapid evolution in small populations, which would leave few fossils.

III. Evidence for the neo-Darwinian synthesis was largely theoretical and mathematical. Using the theory to account for large scale "macro-evolution" required extrapolation.

A. The best field evidence for neo-Darwinian evolution in action came in 1947 from David Lack's study of finches on the Galapagos Islands, the same birds that inspired Darwin. These birds differ primarily in the size and shape of their beaks.

1. Before Lack, naturalists were puzzled by the existence of 13 distinct finch species that appeared to freely mix in a similar environment. Selection theory should allow only the fittest species to survive.

2. Lack propounded that food on various Galapagos Islands differs enough to have favored the evolution of different beaks from the same parental form through a selective process of adaptive radiation.

3. He also found that although different species now mingle on various islands, they do not readily crossbreed. Where similar species inhabit one island, they differ more than normal, suggesting that interspecies competition drives them further apart.

B. Lack's work became the classic case for neo-Darwinian evolution, featured in countless textbooks and documentaries ever since. It remains a case of "micro-evolution," but one involving the evolution of new species and genera.

1. Beginning in 1973 and continuing ever since, field biologists Peter and Rosemary Grant have studied the Galapagos finch population. They have watched average beak shapes and sizes evolve in response to changed conditions.

2. Similar studies of other isolated populations have been found to exhibit a similar pattern of micro-evolution, but the Grants' study remains the most well known.

Essential Reading:

Bowler, *Evolution*, ch. 11.

Supplementary Reading:

Lack, *Darwin's Finches*.

Larson, *Evolution's Workshop*, chs. 6 and 8.

Weiner, *Beak of the Finch*.

Questions to Consider:

1. How did the neo-Darwinian synthesis resolve outstanding questions in evolution theory and lead to the revival of Darwinian mechanisms as the driving force for evolution?

2. Explain why Lack's interpretation of Galapagos finches represents such a classic example of neo-Darwinian evolution in action.

Lecture Ten—Transcript
The Neo-Darwinian Synthesis

Hello, and welcome back. We have been talking quite a bit in the previous lectures over the disputes about evolution, over how evolution operated, over evolutionary mechanisms, both within the scientific community, and to a lesser extent, in the general public.

During the first quarter of the 20th century, scientists remained deeply divided over how evolution operated. They all believed, essentially, that species did evolve. They were deeply divided, however, over how it operated. Virtually none of them saw a significant role for natural selection in the process. By this time, Darwin had won on evolution, but had not won on his particular theory of natural selection.

This is just a reminder of where we have been before. Field naturalists, one important area of evolutionary science, tended to follow Alfred Russel Wallace in stressing the role of geographical isolation and environmental adaptation in evolution. That is, you isolate a species, have it in a somewhat different environment, and a new species will evolve. They tended to see that Lamarckian mechanisms were the cause of variation, however.

Another important area of evolutionary science then and today, of course, is paleontology, the study of fossils. Back then, paleontologists interpreted the fossil record to show, as we've seen, a linear evolutionary development over time. This would be expected under Lamarckianism or orthogenesis, or even theistic evolution. If you go back to the 1910s, 20s, and 30s, most paleontologists tended to be Lamarckians or followers of orthogenesis.

Genetics had become another major area for evolutionary biology. There were some evolutionary biologists, in addition to geneticists, who worked in laboratories. Paleontologists and field naturalists worked out in the field, or in museums, with dried specimens.

By about 1900, but the 1920s, certainly, geneticists and these laboratory biologists tended to reject Lamarckianism for various reasons, pushed by people like August Weissmann, whom we mentioned before. They also leaned in favor of discontinuous, Mendelian-type mutations that fed evolution. Evolution came from these mutations, with really very little role for the adaptive value of those mutations in a "survival of the fittest" selection process.

This reflected the fact that they were working in laboratories. Remember that the most famous geneticist of the time was probably Thomas Hunt Morgan; we mentioned him before. He worked with fruit flies. All of those fruit flies had plenty of food, especially the mutant forms. He wanted to keep them alive and see what the next generation would do. There really isn't much struggle for survival in a laboratory, so they didn't see a whole lot of that. They tended to stress role of the mutations themselves in driving the evolutionary process. Again, this worked well in laboratories, but simply did not work well in the wild. The wild was where the field naturalists worked.

We saw a division among who should be agreeing. It was really the cause, more than anything else, of this split in agreeing what the mechanisms were that were driving evolutionary science. They were working in different fields. There wasn't much speaking to each other.

Aspects of each of these views began merging in the 1920s into a comprehensive neo-Darwinian synthesis. As scientists, each of these different groups began gaining a greater understanding of what was happening in the other groups, so that all of them: Naturalists, laboratory geneticists, and to a lesser extent, paleontologists, began to gain greater understandings of genetic factors and geographic factors.

The first steps toward the neo-Darwinian synthesis, which is the theory of evolution that predominates to this day, were taken during the 1920s, as geneticists began appreciating complexity in the genetics of large populations. This requires a little background to discuss what was coming up, but it starts coming through the world of the geneticists again in the 1920s.

Early Mendelians tended to study discontinuous, single-gene traits, such as tall or short pea plants, or red-eyed fruit flies versus white-eyed fruit flies, thinking that single-gene mutations gave birth to new species and more varieties; we have talked about that in an earlier lecture. They had ignored the seemingly continuous variability in large populations. That's where the field naturalists would write them off. Their work was literally irrelevant, because if you were out in the field, you didn't see just tall and short pea plants, or red-or white-eyed fruit flies. You saw nearly continuous variety in the population, differences in a continuous range and array of species. Therefore, field naturalists were not too interested in their work. Of course, what we are really trying to explain is what happens out in the real world, not in the laboratory.

However, increasingly during this period, these laboratory geneticists began recognizing that multiple genes interact to impact any single trait. It usually is not just one gene that causes factors; sometimes, but not usually. Most factors are multiple-gene factors. The laboratory geneticists began discovering these in the laboratory. When there were multiple genes interacting, the results could produce what would seemingly be continuous variation. The analogy they used was a movie; individual frames are really basically a lot of still photographs. However, if you flip through them very quickly, those still frames look like one continuous moving picture. That's what they called a movie back then, of course, a moving picture. It could be the same with genes. If you had a lot of genes interacting, the results, the impact in the real world, would look continuous.

One Swedish geneticist at this time calculated that if just 10 genes impacted a single trait, there might be 60,000 different variations of that trait. This view dispensed with the need to believe in a blending view of inheritance to produce continuing variations. It didn't need to be a blending of the two parents. They could simply be individual genes, multiple genes impacting together, impacting each individual trait. This solved the problem that even beneficial variations were swamped in reproduction, because if there were a lot of little gene changes, those gene changes could remain and continue. If, of course, you had a blending view of inheritance, any beneficial change would be swamped. There's a problem with that view, when dealing with continuous variation.

Minor, nonfatal variations could survive in a population, and beneficial ones could spread throughout the population, if they had survival value, and produce seemingly continuous change. Some geneticists began working with this. Probably the most notable of these was R.A. Fisher, in England. He proposed that a large population of any species contains enormous genetic variability within that population, that there are lots of different genes combining in different ways. It isn't as if each individual should have the same genes. They have slightly different genes. That creates tremendous genetic variability, which would allow that population to evolve gradually in response to environmental changes, so that if conditions became somewhat different, the different genes that are already in that population would manifest themselves, and become apparent.

Even harmful genes, he pointed out, could survive if they were recessive, and if conditions changed so that they were no longer harmful but became beneficial, then they could take hold, and reappear in the population.

J.B.S. Haldane, another British geneticist of the time, offered a classic example of this at work. It has remained in textbooks to this day. This was the example of the peppered moth. It rather explains what Fisher was hypothesizing. It has remained the example that has lasted. People remember it. The peppered moth was a type of moth in England. As the name suggests, it was "peppered," black and white. Because of genetic variability, however, some were predominantly white, almost totally white, and some were predominantly black, almost totally black. Some were somewhere in between.

Historically, in England, they were known to be mostly white. Some had pepper specks on them, and a few were black, but they were mostly white. Over the previous 50 years, it had been noted that the population had changed so that they were almost all black. There were just a few with pepper and some were white. He said that what had happened was that England had industrialized, and this accounted for the change; there had typically been white walls before, so that the white moths would be on a white wall, or white birch trees, so that the birds wouldn't see them. If the birds saw a black one, they would fly right in and eat them.

Now, the same walls that had once been white, and the same birch trees that had once been white, were now black with soot. The black moths were the invisible ones, and the white ones stood out, so the birds swooped in and ate them. Therefore, the moths had evolved, not into a new species, but into a new variety. Peppered moths had changed from mostly white to mostly black, without any mutation at all, simply because of their inherent genetic variability in their population, in response to changed environmental conditions. These were the same geneticists who were pushing down and discounting environment, and pushing mutations. There was no mutation. They were responding to environmental changes.

Naturally, this would ring true to field naturalists. The idea was that genetic mutations circulate in a population even if they confer no benefit, such as darkness in the peppered moth. This allows a species to build up a funded variability to be exploited by selection if conditions change. Therefore, the blackness which had been a harmful trait when the walls were white, becomes a beneficial trait when the walls become soot-covered. Without mutation, you have got at least a distinctly different variety. In this view, genetic mutations and re-combinations add to variability over time, but they do not trigger evolution. This is what field naturalists had been saying.

Finally, geneticists were recognizing the role of the environment, long recognized by naturalists. That was a change, coming from their viewpoint, that contributed to the neo-Darwinian synthesis—the modern view, as it were.

It was also change coming from the other end. Theories about the evolution of large populations did not necessarily interest field naturalists, because when they were out in the field, they noticed that most speciation that occurs in the wild, not in a laboratory, occurs mostly in small populations, isolated out on the fringe of larger populations.

During the 1920s, geneticist Sewall Wright addressed this issue in the United States. Through laboratory experiments with small populations, Wright found that intense inbreeding produces extreme variability in the species. What happens? Large populations don't have that many mutations, but if you inbreed, you have more. He showed mathematically that inbreeding could drive a small, isolated population to deviate from its parent population; if the deviation proves beneficial in an isolated locale, natural selection could generate rapid evolution. That's what field naturalists had been seeing.

Of course, you have the central population of a species filling an area. On the fringes, you have some isolated groups. If they become isolated, naturally the fringe is where the environment is going to be most different, than where the core is. Out in that area, if they get isolated somehow, so that they inbreed quite a bit, they're more prone to mutation. They come up with a mutation that is different but beneficial in that somewhat different environment. They then could thrive there and evolve into a distinctly different species. This is most likely where speciation would occur. Of course, this is what field naturalists had been saying had been happening. Wright was working in the laboratory.

In 1937, Theodosius Dobzhansky applied Wright's theory to wild populations. He found that given the reservoir of variability, this is already in a population if it is complex and there are lots of traits, and lots of genes involving each trait; with this variability, natural selection could cause gradual evolution under changed conditions. This would be a process that would happen; he worked it out how that would happen in the wild. You would get them isolated; this natural variability would cause those isolated smaller populations to change if the environment was different.

By the early 1940s, the influential British science writer Julian Huxley brought together these various insights, of Dobzhansky, of Wright, Fisher, and of Haldane, some coming from genetics, and some coming from evolutionary biology, into what he called the "modern synthesis." This is what we now generally call neo-Darwinian synthesis.

That was coming mostly out of genetics, though it fit what people, what field naturalists, were seeing in the wild. Well, who's going to bring in the field naturalists?

Though many people were involved, most work was attributed now to the great field naturalist Ernst Mayr. In 1942, he agreed, in a major work, that this new genetics could explain the evolution of isolated populations without invoking Lamarckianism. He had been a former Lamarckian himself. Simply by using Darwinian mechanisms, this could explain what he had seen. There was certainly no field naturalist more respected for his work, mostly with birds. He had worked with other species in the East Indies and around the world.

This view stressed that speciation occurs only through an initial phase of geographical isolation. Without crossbreeding, each population could develop each separate trait, and as they develop that trait, they would deviate further and further, until they would no longer crossbreed when they were brought back together. In a common population, if some got isolated and began to change—either because they no longer physically could crossbreed, or they no longer have the interest in crossbreeding—they wouldn't crossbreed.

These reproductively isolated varieties, subspecies, or closely related species would literally have evolved to fit their separate environments in a process that became known as "adaptive radiation." That's the name that is still applied to it. Then, he threw in an extra insight. If these separate types that have evolved to fit their environment—for instance, variability to feed on a particular food in an isolated environment, or the ability to flee from predators in the altered environment—then began thriving, they would spread out. They might spread out back into their original domain.

If they still reproduce, of course, they would blur back into a similar species, reconnected. If they cross back over, and they remain distinct, they would tend to deviate from each other even more. Let's say, for instance, that there is different food in two different locations. Each had changed to fit their own environment; a common species had remained on one type of food, with the new species in another area.

If they spread out into the same area, one is going to be better adapted to one type of food, the other better adapted to the other food. Both will specialize in their own foods, and they will kind of divide up the available food. By dividing up, they will specialize further, so that where they overlap, they will be different than where they are alone, because if they are alone, they will be exploiting the entire food supply that fits their range, which will be some of the other types. Thus, they will be more different where they cross over.

This was the view of how competition would work in crossover places, and adaptive radiation would work in the separate environments—the environments being the key to evolution, and genetic variability making it possible, with the environment triggering it.

In a comment that describes this, Mayr concluded a new definition of species: "A new species develops if a population which has become geographically isolated from its parent species acquires during this period of isolation characters which promote or guarantee reproductive isolation when the external barriers break down." Seen in this way, a species is no longer an ideally created archetype. No, a species becomes a range of gene frequencies within a reproductively isolated population. Evolution occurs whenever the range in gene frequencies shifts. It is—it becomes—what Darwin wanted all along; what indeed, the ancient Greek atomists wanted all along: a purely materialistic, chemical process.

Led by George Gaylord Simpson in 1944, the paleontologists signed on. They were the last group to sign on to this compromise, or this synthesis. Simpson concluded that this neo-Darwinian view of origins did not necessarily conflict with the fossil record. The fossil record still showed mostly stasis, mostly non-change in a species, with the abrupt appearance of new species, and few transitional forms. They could be put together, however, by viewing that the gaps in the fossil record could be due to the rapid evolution in small populations—which was what was being proposed—but because it was rapid evolution in small, isolated populations, they wouldn't have left many fossils. That would explain the gaps in the fossil record. The fossil record really didn't reinforce the neo-Darwinian synthesis, but the fossil record could be reconciled with the neo-Darwinian synthesis. With this, most paleontologists signed on, and left their neo-Lamarckian traditions.

Evidence for the neo-Darwinian synthesis was largely theoretical. Much of it was mathematical. Using the theory to account for large-scale, what some people call "macro-evolution," required extrapolation, because in all of the situations, we're dealing with similarly-related species, or simply varieties, as with the peppered moth. If you wanted to use it to explain how the evolution of whole new orders or kingdoms occur, you would have to extrapolate that this process just extended over time, but just happens on a larger scale.

The best actual field evidence for the neo-Darwinian evolution in action came in 1947, from David Lack's study of finches on the Galapagos Islands. Interestingly, these are the very same birds that had inspired Darwin a century earlier. Indeed, this field evidence, since most of the rest is theoretical and mathematical, makes sense and seems to fit. This evidence became what was adopted as the public face of neo-Darwinian synthesis. It is what is still seen in most biology textbooks. You read about the peppered moth in biology textbooks, and you read about what became known as "Darwin's finches"—13 different species of finches found on the Galapagos Islands.

What makes these different species distinct is the differences in the size and shape of their beaks. Before Lack, most naturalists were puzzled by the existence of 13 distinct finch species that appeared to freely mix in the similar environment of the Galapagos Islands.

Selectionist theory should only allow the fittest to survive. Darwin had originally posited that there were 13 different species which came from different islands, and so their environments must be somewhat different. That is, indeed, what happens with the Galapagos mockingbirds. However, the more people looked back, they saw that these finches were not on different islands. They're living on the same islands, and the environment seems similar, as does the food. Why don't only the fittest survive?

Because of that, Darwin, though he mentioned the finches in his early writings, such as *The Voyage of the Beagle*, didn't mention it in *The Origin of Species*, because it didn't really work. Then he talked about Galapagos mockingbirds, which do isolate onto separate islands.

Lack, when he looked back at those finches, propounded that the food on the various Galapagos Islands differs enough to have favored the evolution of different beaks from the same parental form through a selective process of adaptive radiation, just as described by Ernst Mayr, Julian Huxley, and the rest. One parental type of finch came over to the Galapagos Islands, and now, on the different islands, they evolve, because the food is slightly different, into different species.

Of course, if that is what had happened historically, what has happened is that they now exist on common islands; they thrived, and then they spread out. Now, they mingle on the same islands, yet they still do not readily crossbreed. In addition, if the neo-Darwinian synthesis is right, then on the islands where they both live, they should be more different from each other than if you took a case from an island where only one existed, and another island where yet another one existed. They don't all live on all the islands. They overlap on some islands. Some are just on one island, some are on multiple islands. Sometimes they cross, and sometimes they don't.

He found exactly what the neo-Darwinian synthesis projects; that is, that when they're alone on an island, they fit their normal type; when they overlap on an island, they're more different from each other—they deviate more. The beaks push one way or the other. The bigger beaks are bigger, or they are smaller beaks. If they have smaller beaks, they're also smaller. Interspecies competition drives them apart.

Lack's work became the classic case for neo-Darwinian evolution. It has been featured in countless textbooks and documentaries ever since. It remains the classic case for micro-evolution, and one that involved evolution of a new species, and even new, closely-related genera. They're all in the same subfamily, but they actually even cross species lines.

At the end of his great book, called *Darwin's Finches*, Lack concludes what he is saying. He writes:

> "The evolutionary picture presented by Darwin's finches is unusual in some of its details, but fundamentally, it is typical of what I believe to have taken place in other birds. Darwin's finches form a little world of their own, not, however, a peculiar world, but one which intimately reflects the world as a whole, so that with these birds, as Darwin wrote, 'We are brought somewhat nearer than usual to the great fact, that mystery of mysteries, the first appearance of new beings on Earth.'"

The work on Darwin's finches has continued, because they're such a perfect test case for the whole neo-Darwinian synthesis, because there are a whole bunch of classically isolated environments nearby each other, with parental species coming in, spreading out onto the different islands, and re-overlapping onto similar islands. The work on those continues to this day.

Beginning in 1973, two field biologists, now working at Princeton, but then from McGill in Canada, Peter and Rosemary Grant, studied this finch population: where they overlap, and where they separate. They have literally watched the average beak shapes and beak sizes evolve in response to changed conditions. When conditions have gotten wetter, the average beak size changes in response to the different types of seeds available. When conditions have gotten drier, the average beak size changes again. Of course, it is not same individual's beak that is changing, but the beaks of the average ones that survive. There's enormous death occurring in the Galapagos, because when it is wet, certain types of finches do not thrive as well as other types of finches. The types that do will survive. When conditions change to a different type, thriving finches change again. If you take the average, they have literally mapped and watched the beak size change.

Similar studies of other isolated populations, such as in Canada and Brazil, in Madagascar, have been found to exhibit a similar pattern of micro-evolution. The Grants' study, David Lack's study, and the Galapagos finches remain the best known.

Lecture Eleven
Scientific Creationism

Scope:

Commemorating the centennial of Darwin's *On the Origin of Species* in 1959, scientists hailed the triumph of a consensus theory of evolution. They largely ignored the persistent anti-evolutionism that marked conservative Christianity in America and assumed that it would die. If anything, however, the rise of neo-Darwinism heightened tensions between traditional religious beliefs and modern scientific thought. Those tensions underlay the prenominal impact of *The Genesis Flood*, a 1961 book in which Virginia Tech engineering professor Henry Morris argued that scientific evidence supported the biblical account of creation.

Morris's brand of scientific creationism swept through America's conservative Protestant churches during the 1960s and 1970s, reviving belief that God created the universe and all species in the past 10,000 years. Rather than simply opposing evolution theory, believers now offered an alternative view for inclusion in public education. With the rise of the Christian Right in American politics, creationists got their way in many places until 1987, when the U.S. Supreme Court overturned creationist instruction as violating the separation of church and state.

Outline

I. The centenary of *Origin of Species* in 1959 marked a triumphant moment in evolutionism. Publications and ceremonies hailed Darwin's contribution in shaping the modern world.

  A. The neo-Darwinian synthesis had gained near universal acceptance among biologists by 1959, giving the impression that scientists fully understood how evolution worked.

  B. Acting to reverse the long-term impact of American's anti-evolution crusade on the content of public science education, in 1959, the federal government began funding high school biology textbooks that emphasized neo-Darwinian evolution.

  C. Neo-Darwinists Julian Huxley in Britain and G.G. Simpson in the United States popularized the expansion of the new synthesis into a humanistic worldview.

1. They saw science as the only source of truth and evolution as an ethical principle. They urged humanity to take hold of the evolutionary process.
2. For Huxley, evolution was a progressive force generating forms that were ever more able to transcend their environment. Taking this as an ethical goal, he valued the freedom to realize life's potentialities as the greatest good.
3. Simpson saw evolution producing beings of ever-greater awareness. For him, the goal became knowledge, which humans could use for the general good.

II. Evolutionists ignored societal shifts that by 1959 had closed large segments of the American population to the theory of evolution. Darwinism's public revival triggered a strong and enduring reaction among conservative Christians.

A. Largely invisible to America's cultural elite, theologically conservative strands of American Protestantism steadily increased in size and influence from 1920 to 1960.
1. Militantly literalistic and Pentecostal Protestant sects existed on the fringes of society before 1920 but grew steadily thereafter. They often had untrained ministers.
2. As the clergy in America's mainline Protestant denominations became more liberal during the 20th century, many conservative parishioners moved to denominations committed to biblical inerrancy.
3. The South, where the conservative Baptist churches dominated society and politics, gained economic, cultural, and political importance in the United States. More people moved south and Southern ways spread nationally.
4. As churches offering clear scriptural authority or ecstatic emotional experience grew, they developed their own colleges, schools, publishing houses, journals, camps, and evangelistic associations.

5. The secularization of Western society that emptied European churches so sapped the vitality of liberal American Protestantism that it did not counter evangelicalism, fundamentalism, and Pentecostalism. Many scientists left the church.

B. Darwinism remained an anathema to conservative Protestants, but they kept their objections within their own subculture until the 1960s, when the appearance of new federally funded biology textbooks ignited protests by parents and churches.

    1. Citing the likes of Huxley and Simpson, conservatives objected to a supposedly atheistic theory being taught as scientific truth in public schools.

    2. By the mid-1960s, fundamentalists were again protesting the teaching of evolution in public schools and demanding that "equal time" be given to their views.

    3. These protests succeeded in limiting acceptance of the new texts, but recent rulings against religious instruction in public schools barred Bible teaching.

III. Mid-20th-century intellectual developments had driven conservative American Protestantism and evolutionary science even further apart than they had been during the 1920s.

A. On the science side, the materialism of neo-Darwinism was less amiable to reconciliation with religion than earlier neo-Lamarckian or theistic theories of evolution. Further, scientists cared less about reconciling science and religion.

B. On the religion side, expansion of conservative churches coupled with erosion of liberal churches had shifted American Protestantism toward biblical literalism. Conservatives showed less interest in reconciling modern science and scriptural interpretation.

C. Conservative Protestant theology on the age of the earth illustrates the rise of biblical literalism.

    1. During the 1800s, in response to geologic evidence of past epochs, many evangelical theologians equated the days of creation in Genesis with geologic ages and accepted the idea of an old earth. Bryan still held these views in the 1920s.

2. During the early 1900s, evangelicals often reconciled science and scripture by positing a gap in Genesis to allow for unnumbered geologic ages (and fossils) between the original creation and the recent creation of modern animal life.

3. Before 1960, the leading advocate of a literal reading of the Genesis account was Seventh-day Adventist science teacher George Price. He argued for a recent six-day creation, with a catastrophic flood shaping the earth's geology.

4. Each succeeding idea split the religious view further from mainstream science.

D. Baptist engineering professor Henry M. Morris revived Price's "flood geology" in 1961 and began spreading it widely. Under the name "scientific creationism," Morris's theory effectively co-opted the creationist banner within two decades.

1. As a young man, Morris became convinced that the entire Bible must be literally true or none of it could be trusted. He went on to study hydraulic engineering to learn how a catastrophic water action could affect the earth.

2. With theologian John Whitcomb, Morris published *The Genesis Flood* in 1961. It presented a scientific argument for creation within a biblical chronology and attributed the fossil record to the layer deposits of a single worldwide flood.

3. Virtually ignored by the scientific community, *The Genesis Flood* gained a wide audience in conservative Protestant circles. Morris followed it with a stream of books, articles, tapes, and lectures promoting his ideas to a variety of church audiences.

4. Since 1972, Morris's Institute for Creation Research (ICR) has widely promoted scientific creationism through books and pamphlets, films, lectures, debates, and research. ICR biology textbooks dominate the Christian school market.

5. During the mid-1970s, ICR prepared creationist textbooks (stripped of any reference to a creator) for the public school market. These texts drew the attention of secular scientists and educators and rekindled public battles over biology education.

IV. The battle over scientific creationism (or "creation science") in public education began with the legal argument that it was as scientific as evolution science and ended with the judicial conclusion that it was simply religious dogma.

  A. Morris and his followers freely admitted that teaching creation promotes belief in a creator, but claimed that was the incidental result of teaching scientific evidence supporting the abrupt, non-evolutionary appearance of the universe, life, and species.

     1. Teaching evolution also promotes a philosophical worldview, they added, and is not supported by any better scientific evidence than creation is.

     2. Assuming this position, both could be given "balanced treatment" in public school biology courses without violating the constitutional bar against religious instruction.

     3. This argument had wide appeal. Public opinion surveys found Americans evenly split on the question of origins and strongly in support of teaching both views.

  B. Riding the crest of Religious Right political activism in the late 1970s and early 1980s, three states and many school districts adopted "balanced treatment" laws or policies.

     1. Science, mainstream religion, and civil liberties groups challenged these laws and policies in court, arguing that they violated the separation of church and state.

     2. One by one, each was struck down as unconstitutional, culminating in a 1987 U.S. Supreme Court ruling against Louisiana's Balanced Treatment Act. No law was needed to teach scientific evidence for or against evolution, the Court ruled; therefore, this law must have been passed to promote religion.

3. These rulings ended the teaching of scientific creationism in public schools, but the battle had awakened both sides and re-sensitized school officials to the issue. It fed the Christian academy and home-schooling movements.

Essential Reading:

Numbers, *The Creationists*, chs. 5–15.

Supplementary Reading:

Larson, *Trial and Error*, chs. 5 and 6.

Marsden, *Understanding Fundamentalism and Evangelicalism*.

Toumey, *God's Own Scientists*.

Whitcomb and Morris, *Genesis Flood*.

Questions to Consider:

1. Why did biblical literalism and conservative Protestantism survive and prosper in 20th-century America? Did this involve a rejection of modern science?

2. Among 20th-century American fundamentalists, how did belief that the earth was created within the past 10,000 years effectively displace the belief that the earth has passed through long geologic ages?

Lecture Eleven—Transcript
Scientific Creationism

We've made it 100 years in the history of evolutionary thought. We have two lectures to go. The centenary of *The Origin of Species* in 1959 marked a triumphant moment in evolutionism. Publications and ceremonies around Europe and America hailed Darwin's contribution to shaping the modern world. We couldn't escape it at the time. There were cover stories in *Time Magazine* and *Newsweek*; *National Geographic* ran special features, as did the major networks: The BBC in England, and the television networks in America. It was a triumphal moment.

The neo-Darwinian synthesis had gained near-universal acceptance among biologists by 1959, giving the impression that scientists fully understood how evolution worked. Acting to reverse the long-term impact of America's anti-evolution crusade on the content of public science education in 1959—partly in response to pressure from scientists, and all of the public attention paid evolution and Darwin at that time—the federal government began funding a new series of high school biology textbooks that emphasized neo-Darwinian evolution. Up to this time, as a lingering effect of the anti-evolution crusade, most textbooks had simply ignored the subject of origins, not wanting to touch a nerve in the buying public, meaning local school boards and parents who would influence the decisions of the local school boards.

Now, the federal government was stepping in to break this deadlock, at the urging of scientists, in a new series. They were called the "BSCS" textbooks. There were several versions, and they were heavily evolutionary.

Neo-Darwinists such as Julian Huxley in Great Britain, whom we've talked about, and George Gaylord Simpson, a paleontologist in the United States, whom we've also talked about in an earlier lecture, popularized the expansion of this new biological synthesis into a broad, all-encompassing, humanistic worldview. Simpson, Huxley, and many other biologists at the time saw science as the only real source for truth—not revealed religion. They saw evolution as an ethical principle within science. They urged all people—all humanity—to take hold of the evolutionary process, and shape it for the good of society.

Huxley and Simpson were predominant in the public mind at this time, writing books, giving lectures, featured at these centennial exhibitions and conferences, papers, hailing 100 years of *The Origin of Species*.

For Julian Huxley, evolution was a progressive force, generating forms ever more able to transcend their environment. Taking this as an ethical goal for life—for humans in particular—he valued freedom to realize life's potential as the greatest good. He would even call it a "humanistic religion," a non-revealed religion, a religion coming from science. He was at a perfect point to propose it. Not only was he a noted scientist, but after World War II, he had been appointed the first director, the founding director of UNESCO, the United Nations Educational Scientific and Cultural Organization. He used this as a world platform to promote his humanistic religious views. He was a signer of the Humanist Manifesto and was involved in popularizing these views throughout the Western world, and pushing it into countries through the work of the United Nations.

George Gaylord Simpson was slightly different. He saw evolution producing beings of ever greater awareness. To him, that's where evolution was leading. For him, the goal became knowledge, which humans could use for the general good.

Again, it was a triumphant moment in evolutionism, a feeling that their view had won, and they should spread out beyond science to the general culture.

In their triumph, evolutionists in America utterly ignored societal shifts that by 1959 had closed large segments of the American population toward the theory of evolution. Darwinism's public revival—that is, the appearance in all of these media such as periodicals and TV—this hard-core Darwinism was often proposed and propounded by people who wanted to carry it beyond biology into an entire worldview, into a philosophy, into a religion, of sorts.

All of this, coupled with the reappearance of Darwinism in textbooks—public school textbooks that their children were reading—triggered a strong and enduring reaction among American conservative Christians. That requires a little background in religious history, to see what had happened in American religion.

Largely invisible to America's cultural elite, theologically conservative strands of American Protestantism had not withered like they expected, but actually had steadily increased in size and influence in America from 1920 to 1960. A variety of factors contributed to this historic development.

Militantly literalistic and Pentecostal Protestant sects existed largely on the fringes of American society in 1920. There were some mainline, solid denominations like Methodists, Lutherans, Episcopalians, Presbyterians, and Baptists, which had dominated Protestant religion in America. The Pentecostal sects, these literally militant sects, groups like the Assemblies of God, were pretty much on the fringes. They generally had untrained ministers, ministers that had been called to the ministry but had never gone to seminaries where they would be exposed to modern ideas of biblical interpretation, and evolutionary views of religion.

What had happened since 1920 can just be followed in the census data. These denominations grew larger and larger. They clearly appealed to vast numbers of Americans, who either were not churched before, or who didn't find the more educated, increasingly liberal denominations of America—the mainline denominations—appealing and satisfying to their needs in religion.

As the clergy of America's mainline Protestant denominations became more liberal through the 20th century—this was a product that we had talked about before, where we saw the split in the 20s within the churches, between the liberals and the modernists on one side, and the fundamentalists, evangelicals or conservatives on the other side, over questions of how to interpret the Bible, how to understand religion, how to understand God—as this happened, many conservative parishioners moved to denominations more committed to biblical inerrancy. They moved toward more conservative denominations, and out of the old mainline denominations, the Methodists, the Episcopalians, and the other churches. The more conservative churches—conservative denominations—tended to grow.

Then, there was the South. The South was the one region of the country where conservatism had won in the fundamentalist/modernist split. When the smoke had cleared in the battle, most of the mainline churches had gone more liberal in the split, and accepted this more evolutionary view of religion. The southern mainline denominations had remained on the conservative side, particularly the Southern Baptist church, Southern Presbyterian Church, and Southern Methodist church.

Then, during the 20th century, there had simply been a growth in the importance of the South. The South had gained economic, political, and cultural importance, thanks, probably more than anything else, to air-conditioning. As more people could live in the South, then the economy could thrive there. More people moved south and moved into these more conservative churches, and Southern ways spread nationally.

As churches offering clearer scriptural authority or charismatic emotional experience grew, they developed their own infrastructure: their own colleges, their own schools, publishing houses, journals, camps, and evangelistic associations that would reach out, often crossing denominational lines, that would unite conservatives.

Before that, most of these structures, such as publishing houses and churches, church colleges, church schools, journals, and camps were denominational. Now they had become interdenominational, but with a conservative bent. This opened this interdenominational network where biblical inerrancy was central.

Therefore, on that side, we've seen an institutional, structural buildup of conservative Protestantism in America, from the 1920s, continuing on to the present day.

On the other side, the secularization of Western society that virtually emptied European churches—so that almost no one in Western Europe goes to church anymore—so sapped the vitality of liberal American Protestantism that it simply was not able to counter evangelicalism, fundamentalism, or Pentecostalism.

The liberal churches withered. Fewer people were going to them. In addition, interestingly, as more people pulled out of the church, it became less of a central role of the cultural elite. Many scientists pulled out of the church, so that early in the 20th century, most scientists—like Robert Millikan, whom we mentioned in an earlier lecture—visible scientists, notable scientists would encourage the church to engage new science.

These scientists were often in the liberal churches, and after this, the liberal churches didn't have many members who were scientists, and they were not pushing the churches to engage science. Because of this, the liberal side of Christianity virtually pulled out of the battle over science and religion. Conservative Christianity in America grew, and liberal Christianity declined in its cultural importance.

Throughout this process, Darwinism remained an anathema to conservative Protestants, but they largely kept their objections within their own subculture that I described previously: Their own camps, colleges, schools, and publishing houses. Their own efforts stayed within that subculture until the 1960s.

The appearance of these new federally funded biological texts that I talked about—these heavily evolutionary texts—ignited protests from the parents and churches, when they saw these textbooks coming to the schools. They had been living in a subculture where evolution was certainly not accepted, largely ignored, and suddenly, their children were coming home with textbooks; where the previous textbooks had largely avoided the issue of biological origins, the new biology textbooks were becoming heavily evolutionary in content. This created and ignited reactions, inciting the likes of Huxley and Simpson, damnable examples; examples of scientists who were trying to push their science beyond biology into all the realms of how we should live in society.

Conservatives objected to this supposed atheistic theory, one that's not just a theory; it is also gave a cultural and social worldview. They objected to this theory being taught as scientific truth in public schools. By the mid-1960s, fundamentalists were again protesting the teaching of evolution in public schools, and demanding that equal time be given to their viewpoints.

Those protests ignited reactions all over America, in Arizona, California, West Virginia, the South, and the Midwest. These protests succeeded in limiting the acceptance of these new textbooks in many places. As we will see, however, constitutional principles that oppose the teaching of religion in public schools would play a role in barring this attempt to get "equal time" for the creationist viewpoint. In short, these parental reactions were successful in the years to come, helping to keep out the evolutionary texts. They could never quite succeed in getting their own viewpoints in, however, because of constitutional problems.

These developments had created a new situation. Let's look at how much religion and science have split apart. There hasn't been a process, at least in America, for the joining of science and religion, like many people on both sides had hoped. Instead, there's been a splitting apart. A whole variety of mid-20th-century intellectual developments have driven this revived and growing conservative American Protestantism away from evolutionary science, even further apart than they were in the 1920s.

It happened on both sides. On the side of science, the materialism of the neo-Darwinian synthesis was simply less amicable to reconciliation with religion than earlier neo-Lamarckian, orthogenesis, or theistic theories of evolution had been. Further, scientists simply cared less about reconciling science and religion. If you could go back to the turn of the 19th century, you would see many scientists engaged, because they wanted to try to work out a reconciliation, not purely siding with science, but trying to reconcile science and religion.

By the late 1900s, fewer scientists even care about religion. Fewer scientists go to church, and fewer of them are trying to work a reconciliation. Therefore, on the science side, there has been shift toward greater hostility, or to just completely ignoring the topic.

On the side of the religious, there has also been a greater deviation. The expansion of conservative churches, coupled with the erosion of liberal churches, has shifted the center of American Protestantism toward biblical literalism, closer toward biblical literalism than it was 100 years ago. The conservatives also show less interest in reconciling modern science with scriptural interpretation. They have a very high view of scripture, of scripture being the literal truth and the literal word of God, the revealed truth.

Conservative Protestant theology on the age of the Earth illustrates this last factor. I will just use that as an illustration of the move toward a more literalistic reading of the Bible as the mainline conservative Protestant viewpoint.

During the 1800s, as we talked about somewhat in earlier lectures, in response to geologic evidence of past epochs, the works of a whole variety of paleontologists and scientists, like Georges Cuvier, whom I mentioned in the first and second lecture, many evangelical theologians—devout, sincere, Bible-believing evangelical theologians—grew to equate the days of creation in the Genesis account with geological epochs, geological ages. Thus, they grew to accept the idea that the Earth was very, very old, breaking from that traditional view that the world was created within the last 10,000 years.

William Jennings Bryan still held these views in the 1920s, when he led the anti-evolution crusade. During the early 1900s, evangelicals in America often reconciled science and scripture by positing that the Genesis account, the first chapter of Genesis, was not really complete; it says, "In the beginning...," and then it talks about the creation of various different types of living kinds that are around today. These evangelicals posited that there could be a gap between "In the beginning..." and the rest of the account. That would allow for unnumbered geological ages, and a vast array of fossils, to have occurred between the original creation and the more recent creation of modern animal and plant life. That was a widely held belief among evangelical, Bible-believing, conservative Christians, early in the 1900s.

Prior to 1960, in fact, the leading advocates for a literalistic reading of Genesis—that the world was created in six literal days within about the last 10,000 years, using the Genesis chronology to find out the age of the Earth—tended to be in small Protestant sects, like the Seventh-day Adventist Church. None of the large, Protestant, mainline denominations, not even the conservative ones, including the Southern Baptist church and Southern Methodist church, held this view.

In fact, the most visible component of this "young Earth" creation in six literal days was a Seventh-day Adventist science teacher named George McReady Price. He argued for a recent six-day creation with a catastrophic flood—Noah's flood, as it were—shaping the Earth's features and laying down its characteristic fossils, such as dinosaur fossils. His teachings were limited mostly to within Seventh-day Adventist churches and Seventh-day Adventist colleges, however.

This view of a "young Earth" creation, if it became mainstream, would utterly split religion from mainstream science. That is what has begun to happen in the last 40 years. Central in the story of how it has moved from smaller, Protestant sects to a main, conservative Christian belief in America, is a Baptist engineering professor named Henry M. Morris. He revived Price's "flood geology," as it was known, and said that Noah's flood would basically explain our geological features. He revived that in 1961, and began spreading it widely among conservative Protestants, under the name "scientific creationism" or "creation science." With this, Morris effectively co-opted the creationist banner during the 1960s and 1970s.

A little bit about Henry Morris. Henry Morris was a very precise, intelligent, intense young man. He was a Southern Baptist, and he became convinced that the entire Bible must be literally true, or none of it could be trusted. Genesis had to be believed equally with the gospel accounts. Believing this, he focused his career on the study of hydraulic engineering. He went to school to get a Ph.D. in hydraulic engineering, in order to learn what catastrophic water action, like Noah's flood, could do to impact geological features. What impact could it have?

Then, working with conservative Protestant theologian John Whitcomb, in 1961, Morris published the book, *The Genesis Flood*. This book presented scientific arguments for creation within a biblical chronology, within this young Earth, six-day creation chronology, attributing the fossil record and most major geologic features to a single, worldwide flood.

As one could expect, given what I have said about the developments within science and the way science had moved away from being much concerned about religion, this book was virtually ignored by the scientific community. It was not reviewed in scientific journals; it was not engaged by the scientific community.

During the 1960s and 1970s, however, it gained an enormous following within conservative Protestant circles. Morris followed this one book up with a stream of books, articles, tapes, and lectures, promoting his ideas to churches and church members. He traveled throughout the country and spoke in churches. He was a professor; in fact, he was chairman of the engineering department at Virginia Tech, a secular school, but he spoke widely on his ideas, and spread them widely throughout the country.

Then, he compounded his efforts in institutional development. He started in 1972. He got help from Tim LaHaye, who is still a very popular Christian writer. His books sell millions of copies. They're usually on biblical prophecy. Working with Tim LaHaye, Henry Morris founded the Institute for Creation Research, ICR, in 1972. Ever since, it has widely promoted scientific creationism through books, pamphlets, films, lectures, debates, and research. ICR biology textbooks grew to dominate the Christian school market. That's a growing market, because since Protestant Christianity has grown, they've spawned off their own high schools, grade schools, and colleges, and ICR textbooks became dominant in these markets. More and more people and students would learn these ideas.

During the mid-1970s, the ICR prepared a creationist textbook, stripped of any reference to a creator, for the public school market. It was this textbook which began to be adopted by conservative-leaning school boards around the country. It first drew the attention of secular scientists and educators to these developments, and rekindled public battles over biology education; that is, the effort to get these ICR textbooks into public schools.

The battle over creation science or scientific creationism in public education began with the legal argument that creation science was as scientific as evolution science, and ended with the judicial conclusion that creation science was simply religious dogma. Morris and his followers freely admitted that teaching creation promotes belief in a creator. Indeed, for people he worked with, and in his publications, he never tried to cover that up. He believed that deeply. He's a very sincere, honest, and direct person. He claimed, though, that this promotion of belief in a creator and of Christianity was simply an incidental result of teaching scientific evidence supporting the abrupt, non-evolutionary appearance of the Universe, of life, and of species.

His focus was never just on the creation of humans. It's the entire creation account, the entire Genesis account—all animals, plants, the Universe, life itself. He would also add that teaching evolution also promotes philosophical or religious viewpoints. Just look at Huxley or George Gaylord Simpson. Morris would also argue that evolutionary science was not supported by any better evidence that his theory of creation.

Assuming the position both evolutionary science and creation science could be given "balanced treatment" in public school biology without violating the constitutional bar against religious instruction, the Supreme Court had ruled by this time that you can't teach religion in public schools, you can't have school prayer, and if a subject is just religion, you can't teach it. Morris is saying that that is no more religion than the other view; well, I'm no more religious than Julian Huxley.

This argument, presented the way Morris and Morris's supporters could do so, had wide appeal. Public opinion surveys that began to be taken on this issue, because it became an increasingly public issue, persistently found that Americans were evenly split on the questions of origins. About half believed that humans were created recently, much as the Bible says. About half believed that they had evolved. In addition, Americans like fair play anyway, and broadly supported the idea of teaching both views in public schools.

Riding on the crest of the Religious Right's political activism in the late 1970s and early 1980s, the efforts of the moral majority, Pat Robertson and other groups, three states and many school districts adopted so-called "balanced treatment" laws, or "equal time" laws or policies, that would give equal time and balanced treatment to creation science and evolution science. This is when there was a tremendous reaction by the other side.

Science groups, mainstream religious organizations—the northern ones, like Methodists and Episcopalians, committed to their view of religion—and civil liberties groups like the ACLU and the People for the American Way, challenged these new policies and laws in court, arguing that they violated the separation of church and state.

One by one, each one of these laws and policies were struck down in courts as unconstitutional, as promoting religious instruction. It culminated in 1987, when the United States Supreme Court ruled against Louisiana's Balanced Treatment Act. No law was needed to teach scientific evidence for or against evolution, the Court ruled, so that this law, requiring equal time or balanced treatment for creation science, must have been passed to promote religion.

These rulings ended the teaching of scientific creationism in public schools. It was now unconstitutional, but the battle had reawakened both sides, and sensitized school officials to the issue. The exclusion of creation science from public schools further fed the Christian academy and homeschooling movements, where parents could control the type of biology that was taught, and use ICR textbooks. Creationism has fed the recent development of more and more students going to private schools, going to Christian schools, and home schools. The battle, now, was fully engaged and continues to this day.

Lecture Twelve
Selfish Genes and Intelligent Design

Scope:

Americans remain divided by the origins debate. Surveys indicate that half of them believe that God specially created the first humans. Most of the rest affirm that God guided evolution. Only about one in 10 Americans accept the God-less theory of origins that dominates science. For many in the third camp, including the popular science writer Richard Dawkins, a purely neo-Darwinian struggle for survival among randomly mutating genes replaces purposeful design as the source of life's diversity. Others in this camp, such as paleontologist Stephen Jay Gould, question the adequacy of the neo-Darwinian synthesis to account for evolution—but remain confident that wholly materialistic mechanisms can do so.

Creationists counter that evolution remains "just" a theory and worry about the social and religious consequences of believing it. Alternative ideas (or at least scientific objections to materialism) belong in the classroom, they maintain. Even many Americans who reject scientific creationism agree that an intelligent designer should not automatically be ruled out as the source of life and individual species. In America, the debate over origins remains as intense as ever.

Outline

I. The American debate over organic origins continues at many levels. Evolutionary biologists debate how evolution works; social scientists debate its implications for human nature; the public debates if it works at all.

II. Virtually all academic biologists agree that species evolve from pre-existing species and most acknowledge only materialistic factors in the process. Disagreements are in its details.

  A. Failing to see sufficient gradualism in the fossil record to fit a neo-Darwinian pattern, paleontologists Stephen Jay Gould and Niles Eldredge offer a punctuated equilibrium model for evolution.

1. The fossil record displays long periods of stability or equilibrium for organisms punctuated by their rapid replacement by a related type, not the gradual branching pattern suggested by the individual selection of orthodox Darwinism.
2. Eldredge and Gould account for this by proposing that small, isolated populations of a species might evolve rapidly through individual selection and, if then better adapted, could rapidly replace the parental type through species selection.
3. Gould adds that developmental constraints in embryos might channel the course of variations independent of environmental factors, somewhat akin to orthogenesis.
4. Small genetic changes affecting embryos could open new channels of development akin to mutations, thereby causing sharp breaks and new directions in evolution.
5. Punctuated equilibrium accounts for the seeming discontinuity of the fossil record in a fundamentally Darwinian and purely materialist framework.

B. The evolution of seemingly altruistic behavior has long been a source of disagreement among Darwinists and a refuge for theists.
1. Darwin maintained that selection operated at the individual level and struggled to explain why individuals sacrifice themselves for others. Social insects with sterile workers exemplified the problem, but human altruistic behavior (which some attributed to spiritual causes) was the real issue.
2. Neo-Lamarckian biologists accounted for altruism in terms of acquired instincts that helped groups (of which the individual was part) survive. Darwin ultimately fell back on such forms of neo-Lamarckian group selection.
3. Theistic evolutionists and others believing in supernaturalism saw God or spiritual forces as a source for such human traits as love, consciousness, and belief in God.
4. The revival of pure Darwinism in the neo-Darwinian synthesis during the mid-20th century rekindled scientific interest in altruistic behavior.

C. As a result of the incorporation of genetics into the neo-Darwinian synthesis, modern Darwinists enjoyed an advantage over Darwin in explaining altruistic behavior. He could reduce selection no lower than the individual level; they could focus on genes.

  1. To a Darwinist, individual selection fails to explain altruistic behavior even for social animals. For the survival and reproduction of any individual, self-interest trumps helping others so that self-interest should spread throughout the species.

  2. If the gene becomes the focus of selection, then helping others with the same gene can help the gene to survive even at the expense of the individual. In 1964, W. D. Hamilton applied this idea to explain sterile insects helping their fertile sisters.

  3. Applied to social insects, gene selection strikes many as a more rational explanation than somehow assuming that God bestowed altruism on insects. Once the approach is accepted for insects, it can be extended to all social animals, including humans.

D. Carrying gene selection to its logical conclusion, Richard Dawkins sees "selfish genes" as the basic units of selection for all evolution.

  1. A gene is simply a chemical compound—a purely material substance without a will, soul, or purpose. It mechanically replicates itself, with chance variations randomly occurring in the copying process.

  2. Genes survive in organisms, and genes producing reproductively successful traits in those organisms flourish. In a totally mechanistic process, "selfish genes" cause gradual evolution in their host or "robot" organisms. Their survival is our purpose.

  3. Critics counter that the organism, not the gene, interacts with its environment. Evolution must involve organisms and environments, not just genes.

III. Continuing controversy surrounds the extension of neo-Darwinian biology to social scientific thought through sociobiology and evolutionary psychology.

   A. Harvard naturalist E.O. Wilson pioneered the field during the 1970s based on his lifelong study of social insects, particularly ants.

      1. Wilson's 1975 book, *Sociobiology: The New Synthesis*, explores the biological basis of social behaviors concerned with reproduction, as well as survival.

      2. In higher animals, for example, Wilson argues that males gain by aggressively spreading their ample sperm while females gain by guarding their scarce eggs.

      3. While acknowledging differences between humans and other animals, Wilson applies sociobiological techniques to explain human social behavior in his 1978 book, *On Human Nature*. He deals with human aggression, gender differences, and ethics.

      4. Wilson tends to accept what evolution has produced as necessarily good and to warn that humans ignore biologically successful instincts at their peril.

      5. Wilson's ideas received a hostile reception from mainstream social scientists, who saw human behavior as conditioned by the social environment rather than by biology.

   B. By the 1990s, sociobiologic ideas in the form of evolutionary psychology were being used by a new generation of social scientists to explain an ever wider array of human behaviors, ranging from violence to love.

      1. Aggressive behavior in young males, currently so self-destructive, could be held over from mating acts that once benefited in reproduction. Among chimpanzees, for example, the most sexually aggressive male produces the most offspring.

      2. Belief in God, purpose, or an afterlife could make people more willing to sacrifice themselves for their kin, thereby preserving their own genes. Biological kin preference could account for racism and genetic nationalism.

      3. Critics counter that education and individual choices influence human behavior. Even most sociobiologists concede that, because of their large brains, people enjoy a measure of control over their instincts not shared by other animals.

IV. As evolutionary biological and social scientists debate the merits of various materialistic explanations for the origins of species and behaviors, large segments of the American population reject naturalism as a premise for the discussion.

    A. In setting its parameters for biology, the elite National Academy of Sciences asserts that science investigates only materialistic causes. Surveys consistently find that nine out of 10 Americans believe in spiritual causes for life.

        1. Typically, about 50 percent of those surveyed say that they believe God created humans in their present form within the past 10,000 years; 40 percent believe the human body evolved over time with God guiding the process; and 10 percent opt for purely naturalistic evolution.

        2. Surveys of scientists find that most support naturalistic evolution, some accept a role for God in evolution, and almost none accept special creation.

        3. This disconnect between scientific and popular opinion over the nature of science lies at the base of America's continuing controversy over creation and evolution.

    B. Lost in the polarized conflict between materialistic evolution and special creation are those who accept that species evolve from species but see some role for God in the process. Broadly speaking, this is "theistic evolution."

        1. Asa Gray's classic theory of theistic evolution held that God channeled evolution by guiding the process of variation. This intricate theory saw God intimately involved in evolution.

        2. No such precise theories of theistic evolution command support today. The term is loosely used to identify anyone who invokes God at any point in organic origins.

3. For example, geneticist Francis Collins, director of the Human Genome Project, calls himself a "theistic evolutionist." He believes that God used the mechanism of evolution to create humans, but that such human traits as altruistic behavior and longing for God were divinely created.

4. Such Darwinists as Alfred Russel Wallace and David Lack also believed that certain human traits, such as love and consciousness, were specially created in evolved hominids to form humans. The Catholic Church accepts this position.

C. Between theistic evolutionists and special creationists are self-identified "progressive creationists." They believe that God intervened at various points in the geologic past to create the basic life forms that then evolved into the various species.

D. Half of all Americans do not accept any significant role for evolution in the generation of different kinds of plants and animals. At most, they accept the so-called micro-evolution of such nearly similar species as Darwin's finches on the Galapagos Islands.

1. For many Christians, Moslems, and other religious believers, God's revealed word in their scriptures is reason enough to believe in special creation.

2. During the 1990s, a loosely organized group of Christian scholars advanced the idea that species are simply too complex to evolve. While eschewing biblical arguments and chronologies, they saw species as the product of "intelligent design."

3. In this group, law professor Phillip Johnson stresses that science should not a priori exclude supernatural causes for natural phenomena. For him, gaps and abrupt appearances in the fossil record are best explained by special creation.

4. Biochemist Michael Behe claims that organic molecules are too irreducibly complex to have evolved through small, random steps. This is similar to the old argument that such organs as the eye are too complex to evolve in a Darwinian fashion.

5. Johnson and Behe have written popular books pushing their challenge to Darwinism. Their arguments join those of scientific creationists in pushing for limits on the teaching of evolution in public schools.

V. Nearly 150 years after the publication of Darwin's theory of evolution by natural selection, it remains central to the scientific and popular debate over organic origins. Scientists generally accept it and push its applications and implications. Many others see it as fatally flawed.

Essential Reading:
Bowler, *Evolution*, ch. 12.

Supplementary Reading:
Dawkins, *The Selfish Gene*.
Behe, *Darwin's Black Box*.
Gould, *Wonderful Life*.
Johnson, *Darwin on Trial*.
Larson, *Trial and Error*, ch. 7.

Questions to Consider:
1. In what way is Dawkin's selfish-gene theory an inevitable consequence of neo-Darwinism? Is sociobiology a logical consequence of Darwinian thinking?

2. What accounts for the continuing appeal of notions of intelligent design in nature? Is this appeal rational, emotional, or both? Is there a scientific basis for it? Is belief in the intelligent design of organisms incompatible with acceptance of the modern neo-Darwinian theory of evolution?

Lecture Twelve—Transcript
Selfish Genes and Intelligent Design

We've made it to our last lecture. Let me use this last lecture to summarize where we are today in the developing history of the theory of evolution. I'm also going to use a few more quotes today, to let some of the current participants speak for themselves.

The American debate over organic origins continues at many levels. Evolutionary biologists debate how evolution works. Social scientists debate how it impacts human behavior—human nature, as it were. The public debates whether it works at all.

Let's deal with each of these three today in our lecture. First, virtually all academic biologists agree that species evolve from pre-existing species, and most acknowledge only materialistic factors and forces at work in the process. The disagreements are in the details.

They occur in two major areas, but they are the two major areas that we've been hearing about, echoing throughout this entire course, from the very beginning: fossils, and altruistic behavior. Let's look at fossils first.

Failing to see sufficient gradualism in the fossil record to fit a neo-Darwinian pattern, paleontologists Stephen Jay Gould and Niles Eldredge offer a punctuated equilibrium model for evolution. "Look at it," they say. The fossil record displays long periods of stability or equilibrium for organisms, punctuated by their rapid replacement by related types. These are not the gradual branching patterns suggested by the individual selectionism of orthodox Darwinism.

Eldredge and Gould account for this by proposing that small, isolated populations of species might evolve rapidly through individual selection, and if then better adapted, could rapidly replace the parental type. Gould adds that developmental constraints within embryos might channel the course of development; that if embryos are designed a certain way, and there were changes, the embryo could only evolve in a certain direction that the embryo permits, through gradual development. This might channel the course of variations totally independent of environmental factors, somewhat akin to what was once posited by orthogenesis.

Now, small genetic changes impacting embryos would then, Gould posits, open up whole new directions of development that would have the impact almost akin to mutations, thereby causing sharp breaks, and new directions in evolution. Punctuated equilibrium accounts for this seeming discontinuity of the fossil record within a fundamentally Darwinist, and a purely materialistic, framework.

I said that the other area where there has been ongoing discussion among biologists is in regard to altruistic behavior. Ever since the days of Darwin, people have wondered, how could Darwinian altruistic behavior have evolved in a Darwinian process? This has long been an area of disagreement among Darwinists, and a refuge for theists.

Darwin maintained that selection operated on an individual level. He struggled to explain why individuals would sacrifice themselves for their species. We could see why one might, or another might. They might have some sort of basis that would cause them to do so. Then those wouldn't survive, though, and they would not reproduce that type. How, then, could it continue to survive? The selfish in the Darwinian world should triumph and survive. Think of a bird that calls out, and saves other birds, by calling out when it sees the coming of a hawk. That bird is sacrificing for the others. How could that trait, that calling out, have survived?

The best example of this to exemplify the whole problem for Darwin, and really, ever after in evolutionary thought, is social insects. Anthills, bee hives; you'll see these insects sacrificing themselves for the group. Perhaps the most dramatic examples are sterile workers, among these social insects. Why would sterile workers, who can't reproduce, continue? Why would they survive in a Darwinian world?

Even though this was the example often debated, and the one raised while trying to explain this, and though it captured Darwin's attention later in his life, the real underlying issue was human development. How could altruistic behavior exist in humans? That was the real issue. Of course, some people attributed that to spiritual causation. Darwin struggled to find a materialistic basis for it.

Neo-Lamarckian evolutionists didn't have any problem with it. The neo-Lamarckian biologists who dominated the late 19th-century accounted for it in terms of an acquired instinct—acquired behavior that was learned over time, that helped groups, of which the individual was part, to survive. Ultimately, Darwin himself fell back on such forms of neo-Lamarckian group selection to explain altruistic behavior in social instincts, in animals, and in humans.

Theistic evolutionists also didn't have any trouble with this, because they believed that a supernatural cause, God, could have put altruistic behavior, love, selfishness into animals, and into evolved humans. This, of course, was the view of Alfred Russel Wallace.

The revival of pure Darwinism within the neo-Darwinian synthesis, during the mid-20th century, rekindled interest in altruistic behavior. It was not such a focal issue as long as neo-Lamarckianism, orthogenesis, or some other mechanism for evolution predominated.

It came back with a vengeance, though, with the neo-Darwinian synthesis. Due to the incorporation of genetics into the neo-Darwinian synthesis, however, modern Darwinists had an advantage over Darwin in explaining altruistic behavior. Darwin could reduce selection to no lower than the individual level; that is, individuals struggling to survive. Modern Darwinists could reduce it to the genetic level: genes.

To a Darwinist, individual selection fails to explain altruistic behavior even for social insects. For the survival and reproduction of any individual, self-interest trumps helping others. Thus, self-interest should spread throughout the species, and altruistic individuals should not reproduce or survive, and ultimately disappear.

This is a difference that modern Darwinian synthesis has: If the gene becomes the focus of selection, then helping others with that same gene can help the gene to survive, even at the expense of the individual.

In 1964, W.D. Hamilton applied this approach to explain sterile insects helping their fertile sisters. He found that these sterile insects share quite a bit of genetic similarity, many common genes, with their fertile sisters. By helping their fertile sisters survive, their genes survive.

Applied to social insects, gene selection strikes many as a more rational explanation than somehow assuming that God bestowed altruism on insects. Once this approach is applied and accepted for insects, however, it can be extended for all social animals, including humans.

Carrying gene selection to its logical conclusion, Richard Dawkins sees "selfish genes," as he calls them, as the basic unit of selection for all evolution. As he describes it, a gene is simply a chemical compound. That, everyone agrees to. It doesn't matter whether you're a creationist or an evolutionist. A gene is simply a chemical compound, a purely material substance. It doesn't have a will, doesn't have a soul, doesn't have a purpose. It's just a bunch of chemicals, a bunch of molecules put together. A bunch of molecules put together, a chemical molecule.

It mechanically replicates itself, with chance variations randomly occurring in the copying process. Genes survive within organisms, and genes producing reproductively successful traits in those organisms flourish. It's rather like a knight's armor. The armor is the protective device, and it helps to keep a knight alive in battle. Therefore, our bodies, or the bodies of any animal or plant, are the armor for the gene. They help the gene to survive and reproduce, and to make more of its kind.

In a totally mechanistic process, Dawkins explains, selfish genes cause the gradual evolution in their host, or, as he calls them, their "robot" organisms. Their survival—the survival of genes—is our purpose.

To capture this, let me read a bit from Dawkins. He's a beautiful writer, a great expresser of his own ideas. His writings are quite popular. These are Dawkins' views of origin:

> "In the beginning was a self-replicating molecule."

He goes on to write,

> "The next important step link in the argument, one that Darwin himself laid stress on, is competition. The primeval soup was not capable of supporting an infinite number of replicator molecules. Some of them may have discovered how to break up molecules of rival varieties of chemicals, and to use the building blocks so released for making their own copies. Other replicas perhaps discovered how to protect themselves, either chemically or by building physical walls of protein around themselves. This may have been how the first living cell appeared. The replicators which survived were the ones that built survival machines for themselves to live in. Survival machines got bigger and more elaborate,

and the process was progressive. Now, they swarm in huge colonies,"

he's talking about the genes,

"safe inside gigantic, lumbering robots. They are in you, they are in me. They created us, body and mind, and their preservation is the ultimate rationale for our existence. They have come a long way, those replicators. Now they go by the name of 'genes,' and we are their survival mechanism."

Richard Dawkins, describing his selfish gene theory and approach.

Needless to say, this sort of thinking arouses a lot of controversy. I have found people who are quite proud of themselves and their species. Critics counter, many within science, that organisms, not genes, interact with the environment, and therefore, evolution must involve organisms and environments, not just genes. This debate continues.

It logically leads, though, to the second level of debate that I mentioned at the beginning—the debate that goes on among social scientists about the applications of biological theories, evolution theory to human behavior, human nature. This surrounds, in general, the extension of neo-Darwinian thinking to social scientific thought. Its primary focus is on what are called "sociobiology" and "evolutionary psychology." Put simply, does biology control behavior? Or, as *Time Magazine* put it in a cover article not too long ago, is adultery in our genes? Are the various activities we do, our social behaviors, genetically programmed?

Harvard naturalist E.O. Wilson pioneered this field during the 1970s, based on his lifelong study of social insects, particularly ants. Wilson's 1975 book, *Sociobiology: The New Synthesis*—notice the echo to the neo-Darwinian synthesis, modern synthesis—in that book explores the biological basis of social behavior by looking at what would cause success. Success requires not just survival, as Darwin pushed it, but also reproduction. What sort of biological traits would foster survival and reproduction? I'll use Wilson's own words to try to capture that; the way he puts it right at the beginning:

He starts out by writing:

"Natural selection is the process whereby certain genes gain representation in the following generations, superior to that of other genes located in the same chromosomal positions. In the process of natural selection, then, any device that can insert a higher proportion of certain genes into subsequent generations will come to characterize the species. One class of such device promotes prolonged individual survival."

Survival of the fittest.

"Another supports superior mating performance and care for resulting offsprings."

That is, more reproduction, more survivors of the next generation.

"This brings us to the central theoretical problem of sociobiology. How can altruism,"

Again, that is the issue for these people, altruism. Where could altruism come from?

"How can altruism, which by definition reduces personal fitness, possibly evolve by natural selection? The answer is kinship."

Then, he goes into his discussion.

You can see it in a lot of ways, as he's describing his various books and writings. Wilson is, like Dawkins, a wonderful writer, a very popular writer, a very persuasive writer. In higher animals, for example, Wilson argues that males gain by spreading their ample sperm, and thus, this explains aggressive behavior in males. Females gain by guarding their scarce eggs, thus explaining protective behavior as natural for females.

While acknowledging difference between humans and other animals, Wilson applies sociobiological techniques to humans to explain human social behavior. He does this most prominently, initially, most visibly, in his 1978 book, *On Human Nature*. Here, he deals with the biological basis for human aggression, for gender differences, and for our basic ethics. Wilson tends to accept what evolution has produced is necessarily good, and continually warns that humans ignore biologically successful instincts at their peril.

As you can well guess, given the areas that they touch on, Wilson's ideas initially received a very hostile reception from mainstream social scientists who traditionally saw human behavior as conditioned by social environment, rather than biology, and sought to reform human behavior by reforming the environment.

By the 1990s, however, sociobiological ideas in the form of evolutionary psychology were beginning to be used by a new generation of social scientists to explain an ever wider array of human behaviors ranging from violence to love. Aggressive behavior in young males is presently so destructive. How could this have been programmed into humans? How could this terrible, aggressive behavior that so many young males show been genetically programmed? It is self-destructive. How could it have evolved?

It could be a holdover, like a rudimentary organ, from the mating acts that once benefited reproduction. The parallel would be chimpanzees. For example, the most sexually aggressive males produce the most offspring. Sexual practices among chimpanzees are pretty gruesome. Most people would describe them as organized rape.

Wilson and evolutionary biologists tackle other questions. Some of them are very controversial. Wilson explains how belief in God, or belief in purpose to our lives, or belief in an afterlife could make people willing to sacrifice for themselves, and for their kinfolk, thereby preserving their own genes, because our kinfolk share our genes.

Biological kin preference could also account for racism and for genetic nationalism. These are seemingly destructive traits, but they could have a biological basis. Critics counter that education and individual choices influence human behavior. Even most sociobiologists concede that due to their large brains, people enjoy a measure of control over instincts not shared by other animals, particularly social insects. Thus, the debate goes on; the debate continues in this area.

As evolutionary biologists and social scientists debate the merits of various materialistic explanations for the origins of species, and behaviors, large segments of the American population reject the very naturalism that underlies it, and continue to believe in God, the supernatural, or at least that people have a purpose, and that there is a purpose to life. This undercuts the belief in naturalism, that they believe that there must be at least the possibility of non-naturalistic forces that could impact natural phenomena, at least us.

This runs counter to the basic presuppositions of science and creates an ongoing tension between science and society at the turn of the 21st century. In setting the parameters for biology, for example, the elite National Academy of Sciences asserts that science only investigates materialistic causes. Let me read from their statement on this. They state in a recent publication:

> "The statements of science must invoke only natural things and processes."

Then, they go on the quote Ernst Mayr, the great biologist and co-founder of the neo-Darwinian synthesis. He writes:

> "The demarcation between science and theology is perhaps the easiest, because scientists do not invoke the supernatural to explain how the natural world works, and they do not rely on divine revelation to understand it."

Scientists may say that, but the surveys consistently find that nine out of 10 Americans believe in spiritual causes for life, and believe in God. Typically, about 50 percent of people surveyed, if you take surveys on this question in America, believe that God created humans in their present form. Forty percent, or four-fifths of the remainder, believe that human body evolved over time, but that God guided the process. Only 10 percent opt for a purely naturalistic form of evolution for humans. Yet, if you take surveys of scientists, you find this pattern almost upside down. Most support naturalistic evolution, some accept a role for God in the process of evolution, and virtually none accept special creation.

This disconnect, this tension between scientific and popular opinion over the nature of science, lies at the base of America's continuing controversy over creation and evolution. Before I finally close with that tension, let's not forget those lost in the middle.

Between this polarized conflict between materialistic evolution and special creation are those who accept that species evolve from species, but see some role for God in the process. Broadly speaking, this is now what is meant by the term, "theistic evolution." Asa Gray's classic theory of theistic evolution that he developed in the late 1800s held that God channeled evolution by guiding the process of variation. This intricate theory saw God as intimately involved in evolution. No such precise theories of theistic evolution command support today. That was a scientific theory; this is more a general belief or viewpoint. The term is now used conventionally. It loosely applies to identify anyone who invokes God at any point in organic origins.

For example, the geneticist Francis Collins, the director of the Human Genome Project, and a very, very active scientist today, calls himself a "theistic evolutionist." He believes that God used the mechanisms of evolution to create humans, but that such human traits as altruistic behavior, and longing for God, were divinely created.

Such Darwinists as Alfred Russel Wallace and David Lack also believe that certain human traits, such as love and consciousness, were specially created in evolved apes, to create humans. The Catholic Church accepts this position.

Between theistic evolutionists and special creationists are a self-identified group calling themselves "progressive creationists." They believe that God intervened at various points in the geologic past to create the basic lifeforms that then evolved into various types.

Those are the in-between groups, but half of all Americans do not accept any significant role for evolution in the generation of different kinds of plants and animals. At most, this group accepts the so-called "micro-evolution" of such nearly related species as Darwin's finches on the Galapagos Islands. "Sure, those could have evolved, but all of the basic kinds," echoing back to the passage of Genesis in our first lecture, "all of the basic kinds of finches must have been created."

For many Christians, Moslems, and other religious believers, God's revealed word in scripture is reason enough alone to believe in special creation.

Adding to this group, however, during the 1990s there emerged a loosely organized group of mostly Christians who advanced the idea that species are simply too complex to have evolved.

While eschewing biblical arguments and chronologies, they saw species as the product of what they call "intelligent design." This is the so-called "intelligent design movement."

Within this group, University of California law professor Phillip Johnson stresses that science should not a priori exclude supernatural causes for natural phenomena. For him, gaps and abrupt appearances in the fossil record are best explained by special creation.

Phillip Johnson is an active participant in these debates. Performance of this view will often include quotes from his highly popular books. He is as good writer, some ways, as Richard Dawkins or E.O. Wilson. His books are popular sellers. I'll give you a little clue about how he thinks and what he argues. I will read you a little passage from an interview he gave on one of his most popular books:

He says:

> "I concede that Dawkins,"

using Dawkins' theory of selfish gene,

> "achieved his word magic with the very tools that are familiar to us lawyers. He was deciding everything by definitions. We define science as the pursuit of materialistic alternatives. Now, what kind of answers do we come up with? By gosh, we come up with materialistic answers. If you take as a starting point that there is no creator, then something more or less like Darwinism has to be true as a matter of definition."

Therefore, Phillip Johnson argues, "Let's get behind those definitions and allow God in. Allow non-materialistic causes. Allow supernatural causes as a possible answer for what we see in nature." If you exclude it automatically, as the National Academy of Sciences would want to do, you have to come up with Darwin. Let's open the field for discussion, he will argue.

Biochemist Michael Behe, who is also part of this movement, claims that organic molecules are too irreducibly complex to have evolved through the random, small steps of Darwinism. I guess, really, if you look at it closely, it's similar to the old arguments that organs such as the eye are too complex to evolve in a Darwinian fashion, updated for the issues of the evolution of chemical processes and biological processes within organisms, such as the example of blood clotting that he uses. It is that simply any one step in this process wouldn't have survival value, so you couldn't get to the end result without intelligent design.

Johnson and Behe have written popular books pushing their challenge to Darwinism. Their arguments now join those of traditional scientific creationists in pushing for limits on the teaching of evolution as true in public schools.

Nearly 150 years after the publication of Darwin's theory of evolution by natural selection, it remains central to the scientific and popular debate over organic origins. Scientists generally accept it, and push its applications and implications. Many others see it as fatally flawed. There is more history to this story, but it lies in the future.

Timeline

1775 .... German geologist Abraham Werner begins teaching that the earth's features were formed through the gradual retreat of an ancient ocean.

1795 .... Scottish geologist James Hutton proposes that the earth's features are formed through ongoing processes of mountain uplift and erosion over a long time.

1795 .... French naturalist Georges Cuvier begins his work in paleontology and comparative anatomy and finds patterns in the extinction, appearance, and relationships of species over time.

1802 .... The French naturalist Lamarck outlines his theory of organic evolution through the inheritance of acquired characteristics.

1802 .... British theologian William Paley publishes his popular study of natural theology.

1809 .... Charles Darwin is born.

1830 .... English geologist Charles Lyell publishes the first volume of *Principles of Geology*, which posits that current geologic forces acting over long periods of time are sufficient to account for the earth's features.

1831–1835 .... Darwin serves as naturalist aboard H.M.S. *Beagle*, during which time he accepts Lyell's theory of geology and finds evidence of organic evolution.

1838 ....Darwin conceives of natural selection as a driving force for organic evolution through his reading of Thomas Malthus's *Essay on Population.*

1844 ....English writer Robert Chambers publishes his controversial treatise on evolution, *Vestiges of Creation.*

1851 ....English sociologist Herbert Spencer begins publishing a series of books outlining his theory of human progress through an individualistic struggle for survival.

1858 ....British naturalist Alfred Russel Wallace independently conceives of natural selection as a driving force for organic evolution and sends his essay on the topic to Darwin. Wallace's essay is published with one by Darwin.

1859 ....Darwin publishes *Origin of Species,* setting forth his theory of evolution in full.

1865 ....German zoologist Ernst Haeckel begins his efforts to reconstruct a materialistic history of evolutionary progress from the origin of life to the present.

1865 ....English scientist Francis Galton first publishes his eugenic theories of guiding human evolution through selective breeding.

1870s...The discovery of fossil evidence for the evolution of species in the past, notably a nearly complete series of ancient horse species and a toothed, feathered animal supposedly linking reptiles to birds.

1871 ....Darwin publishes *Descent of Man,* extending his materialistic theory of evolution to the development of humans.

1876 ....Alfred Russel Wallace publishes his treatise on the geographic distribution of species.

1882 ....German biologist August Weismann publishes *Studies in the Theory of Descent,* arguing that inheritance and variation occur in germplasm, which is fixed at conception.

1892 ....On the island of Java, Dutch naturalist Eugene Dubois discovers the first known hominid fossils linking humans with other primates.

1900 ....Dutch botanist Hugo De Vries rediscovers Mendelian genetics and applies it to his mutation theory of evolution.

1910 ....American geneticist Thomas Hunt Morgan observes spontaneous inborn variations in fruit flies that are then passed on in a Mendelian fashion, suggesting a genetic basis for evolution.

1925 ....South African paleontologist Raymond Dart discovers fossil remains of an upright-walking early human ancestor, *Australophithecus africanus.*

1925 ....Tennessee teacher John Scopes is tried and convicted for violating America's first anti-evolution law.

1927 ....The United States Supreme Court upholds compulsory state programs for the sexual sterilization of persons deemed eugenically unfit.

1937 ....Ukrainian-born American geneticist Theodosius Dobzhansky publishes *Genetics and the Origin of Species*, which lays the foundation for the modern neo-Darwinian synthesis.

1940s.......................................Nazi practices discredit eugenics.

1942 ....Two major works articulate the modern neo-Darwinian synthesis: Ernst Mayr's *Systematics and the Origin of Species* and Julian Huxley's *Evolution: The Modern Synthesis*.

1947 ....English ornithologist David Lack publishes *Darwin's Finches*, providing critical field evidence for the modern neo-Darwinian synthesis.

1949 ....American paleontologist George Gaylord Simpson publishes *The Meaning of Evolution*, which presents Darwinism as a new foundation of morality devoid of transcendental religious values.

1953 ....British biologist Julian Huxley publishes *Evolution in Action*, which proposes evolutionary humanism as a secular religion.

1959 ....The centenary of the publication of *Origin of Species* marked by triumphal celebration of Darwinism.

1961	British paleontologist Mary Leakey discovers fossil remains of a 2-million-year-old human species, *Homo habilis*, that lived among non-human hominids.
1961	American engineer Henry M. Morris and theologian John Whitcomb publish *Genesis Flood*, which revives interest among conservative Protestants in scientific arguments for accepting the literal truth of the biblical account of creation.
1972	Paleontologists Stephen Jay Gould and Niles Eldredge propose their punctuated equilibrium model of organic evolution.
1973	Naturalists Peter and Rosemary Grant begin their three-decade study of finches on the Galapagos Islands that becomes the leading field study of evolution in action.
1975	American naturalist E.O. Wilson publishes *Sociobiology*, which offers a basis in evolutionary biology for social behavior.
1976	British science writer Richard Dawkins publishes *The Selfish Gene*, which popularizes the idea of evolution operating at the gene level.
1981	Arkansas and Louisiana enact statutes mandating balanced treatment for scientific creationism in public school biology courses.
1987	The United States Supreme Court strikes down the Louisiana

creationism law as an unconstitutional effort to promote religious instruction in public schools.

1991 ....Law professor Phillip Johnson launches the religiously motivated "intelligent design" critique of organic evolution by publishing *Darwin on Trial*.

1990s...Paleontologists in East Africa uncover fossil evidence for several upright-walking, small-brained hominid species living up to 6 million years ago. A branching hominid family tree is extended into the remote past.

Glossary

Baconian science: a method of doing science, traditionally associated with the writing of philosopher Francis Bacon, that finds scientific knowledge coming through inductive reasoning based on observation and experimentation.

Catastrophism: a 19th-century geological theory articulated by Georges Cuvier, Louis Agassiz, and others that saw the earth's history divided into biologically distinct eras separated by worldwide floods or ice ages.

Creationism, scientific (or creation science): a 20th-century development in conservative Protestant thought that seeks scientific evidence supporting a literal reading of the biblical account of creation in the first chapters of Genesis.

Darwinism: a theory of organic evolution developed by Charles Darwin and others stating that biological species develop from pre-existing species through the natural selection and accumulation of hereditary variations in individual organism.

Eugenics: a theory of applied science, popular during the early 20th century, that sought to improve the human race by encouraging breeding by supposedly superior individuals and discouraging breeding by supposedly inferior ones.

Evolution, organic: the scientific theory that new species evolve from pre-existing species through gradual change rather than being abruptly created.

Evolutionary psychology: the view that various human emotions and behaviors, such as gender roles and aggression, are influenced by biological factors rooted in the evolutionary past.

Fossil record: the composite record of past life on earth preserved in remnants or traces of organisms, such as skeletons or imprints, embedded in rocks and soil.

Fundamentalism, Protestant: a strand of conservative Protestant Christianity characterized by a belief in the literal truth of the Bible and an eagerness to defend and propagate that truth.

Genesis account of creation: the description of origins set forth in the opening chapters of the Bible, which states that God created the physical universe, all biological kinds, and humans in His own image.

Hominid: a primate of a family of upright-walking, relatively large-brained animals of which modern humans, or *Homo sapiens*, is the only surviving species.

Intelligent design: the belief that only intelligent design, rather than materialist evolution, can account for the irreducible complexity of organic life.

Laissez faire: an economic and social doctrine that believes in human progress through rugged individual effort unfettered by governmental intervention in the economy or charitable welfare programs.

Lamarckism (or Lamarckian evolution): a theory of organic evolution developed by Lamarck and others stating that biological species develop from pre-existing species through the progressive accumulation of inheritable traits acquired in response to environmental conditions and internal developmental forces.

Materialism, scientific: the philosophic theory in modern science holding that physical matter in motion is the only reality, such that everything in the universe (including consciousness, emotions, and belief in God) can be explained by physical laws without invoking spiritual forces.

Mendelian genetics: the theoretical principles of heredity for sexually reproducing organisms first formulated by Gregor Mendel, which states that both parents contribute traits to offspring that do not blend but express themselves according to fixed laws of dominance or recessiveness.

Mutation theory: a theory of organic evolution developed by Hugo De Vries and others stating that biological species develop from pre-existing species through chance inheritable mutations that quickly create a distinct breeding population.

Natural selection: a scientific theory separately derived by Charles Darwin and Alfred Russel Wallace that accounts for organic evolution through the higher reproductive rates of individuals in a species that possess an inheritable variation rendering them better able to survive in their environment.

Natural theology: the belief that the existence and character of the creator is displayed in the creation, such that design in nature proves the existence of God and can provide a basis for theological understanding.

Neo-Darwinian (or modern) synthesis: a theory of evolution that sees a species as an array of similar individuals containing a range of genetic variations that can be acted on by natural selection to generate shifts in gene frequencies such that new species can result, especially in isolated populations or in response to environmental changes.

Neo-Lamarckism: variant theories of organic evolution developed in the late-19th century that typically incorporated Lamarckian concepts of variation (including the inheritance of acquired characteristics) with Darwinian notions of natural selection to explain the development of new biological species from pre-existing ones.

Orthogenesis: a theory of organic evolution developed in the late 19th century stating that biological species develop from pre-existing species in a progressive pattern arising from internal developmental forces that operate independent of external factors.

Punctuated equilibrium: a version of Darwinian evolution theory proposed by paleontologists Stephen Jay Gould and Niles Eldredge beginning in the 1970s to account for the abrupt appearance and subsequent stability of species in the fossil record by supposing that new species develop in small isolated populations that then can spread rapidly through species selection.

Selfish genes: a version of neo-Darwinian evolution theory that sees genes (rather than individual organisms) as the basic unit of selection, such that organisms evolve as a means to facilitate the survival of their genes, which can account for seemingly altruistic behavior by individuals on behalf of their kin.

Social Darwinism: a loosely defined term used by critics to ridicule any late-19th-century social and economic policies and practices that assumed human progress came through a competitive survival-of-the-fittest process among individuals, nations, or races.

Sociobiology: the view that Darwinian theories of evolutionary biology, featuring a competitive struggle for survival among individuals and successful reproductive strategies for individuals, provide a basis for understanding societal behavior patterns of individuals, including those of humans.

Theistic evolution: the view that God designed, guides, or intervenes in the evolutionary process to produce some or all species over time.

Uniformitarian geology: the theory that the earth's geologic features are the result of existing natural geologic forces (such as uplift and erosion) operating uniformly over eons of geologic history from the formation of the earth to the present time, without the need for supernatural or dramatically different interventions in the past.

Biographical Notes

Agassiz, Louis (1807–1873). Born in Switzerland, Agassiz first gained international fame for his pioneering study of fish fossils, research that brought the ancient seas back to life through the description of their inhabitants. His later study of glaciation led to the modern understanding of ice ages. Moving to the United States in 1846, Agassiz accepted a professorship at Harvard, where he trained a generation of American naturalists and published a steady stream of popular and scientific books. His 1859 *Essay on Classification* was perhaps the most comprehensive explanation of species ever compiled from a separate creation viewpoint. In it, he argued that because of their innate complexity, species must be fixed within definite limits and unchanging over time. Thereafter, he remained the leading scientific critic of evolution theory.

Bryan, William Jennings (1860–1925). A product of the American Midwest, Bryan was a populist politician and renowned orator. After two terms in Congress, the Democratic Party nominated Bryan for president in 1896, the youngest person ever so nominated by a major political party. His stands for workers' rights, business regulation, and monetary reform earned him the lasting support of many farmers, miners, and factory workers. After a narrow defeat in 1896, the Democratic Party re-nominated him in 1900 and again in 1908, but he lost by ever-wider margins. Serving as Secretary of State from 1913 to 1915, Bryan tried to keep the United States from entering the First World War. Seeing social Darwinism as a source for regressive social, military, and political policies, Bryan lobbied for laws against teaching the Darwinian theory of human evolution in public schools, culminating in the Scopes trial of 1925, in which he served as co-prosecutor.

Cuvier, Georges (1769–1832). French naturalist Georges Cuvier pioneered modern comparative anatomy and paleontology from his posts at the Museum of Natural History in Paris and the College of France. His study of comparative anatomy stressed the functional fit of animals to their environment and led to his classification of all animals into four viable body types. His study of paleontology both established the existence of vast numbers of extinct animals unlike any animals living today and identified fundamental breaks in the fossil record. Combining these views, Cuvier denied the possibility of evolution and postulated instead that the earth underwent a series of catastrophic extinctions, followed by the appearance of new species based on similar basic forms. Backed by impressive research in fossils and anatomy, Cuvier's theories gained a wide following among naturalists during the first half of the 19th century.

Darwin, Charles (1809–1882). Born into a wealthy, well-connected British family, Darwin was educated at Edinburgh and Cambridge universities, where he excelled in the study of natural history. From 1831 to 1836, he served as the volunteer naturalist aboard H.M.S. *Beagle* on its voyage around the world. The observations and collections that Darwin made during this trip provided the basis for a lifetime of private scientific research and earned him entry into the British scientific establishment. They also convinced him that species must evolve from other species, a theory that he worked on in secret for more than 20 years following his return to Britain. Finally publishing his complete theory of evolution by natural selection in 1859, Darwin transformed the biological sciences. Living a secluded life at his country home, Darwin continued to defend and extend his theory until his death.

Dobzhansky, Theodosius (1900–1975). Born and educated in the Russian empire, Dobzhansky emigrated to the United States in 1927 to work with the legendary American geneticist Thomas Hunt Morgan, who then led a team of researchers seeking to combine Darwinian evolution with Mendelian genetics. Dobzhansky's 1937 book, *Genetics and the Origin of Species*, was the first substantial synthesis of the two subjects. Utilizing mathematical models and experimental observations, his synthesis explored the evolutionary potential of existing genetic variability in wild populations. Rather than having to wait for random variations to occur, then selecting those that are beneficial, Dobzhansky showed that the inherent variability in the gene pool allows species to evolve rapidly through natural selection in response to environmental changes without the need for any new variations. Dobzhansky's work inspired a generation of geneticists, naturalists, and evolutionary biologists, culminating in the modern neo-Darwinian synthesis of modern biology.

Dubois, Eugene (1858–1940). A religious skeptic from the Catholic-dominated southern provinces of the Netherlands, Dubois devoted his scientific career to proving the theory of evolution. Following Ernst Haeckel, he studied the comparative anatomy of the larynx as a means to explore the evolution of human speech. Frustrated by the slow progress of this research, he resigned his post at the University of Amsterdam in 1887 and moved to the Dutch East Indies to look for fossil evidence of intermediate species in the evolution of humans from apes. The lack of such evidence at the time stood as a major obstacle to popular acceptance of evolution theory. In 1891 on Java, Dubois succeeding in finding the first hominid fossils ever collected. He called his discovery *Pithecanthropus erectus* in honor of Haeckel's hypothetical ape-man. Like Haeckel, Dubois favored Lamarckian forms of evolution theory. This rendered his theoretic work of little lasting scientific significance, but for decades, *Pithecanthropus* remained the best fossil evidence for human evolution.

Galton, Francis (1822–1911). An independently wealthy gentleman-scientist, Galton gained fame as the "father" of eugenics. Born in Birmingham, England, Galton attended Cambridge University but never graduated from it. Instead, he traveled in Africa and gained entry to the elite Royal Society of London as an ethno-geographer on the basis of his travel writings. Following the publication of *Origin of Species* by his cousin, Charles Darwin, Galton became an ardent supporter of the theory of evolution and made his life's work the applications of its teachings to guiding the evolution of humanity through controlled breeding. He coined the term "eugenics" for this science and developed modern statistical methods to study it. Through his books, articles, and research, he championed the goal of more children from healthy, intelligent, and handsome parents and fewer children from unhealthy, unintelligent, and ugly ones.

Haeckel, Ernst (1834–1891). Born in Prussia and educated at Wurtzburg and Berlin, Haeckel was a political radical who saw Darwin's rejection of design in nature as a weapon to battle the established structure of German society and religion. Integrating Lamarckism with Darwinism, Haeckel saw biological races progressively formed in direct response to environmental factors, then screened by a competitive struggle that allowed only the fittest of them to survive. As a scientist, he studied evolutionary relationships in the embryonic development of species, finding similarities that long stood as important evidence for evolution. Pushing evolution theory back to the origin of life, he speculated about the physical factors that gave birth to life from inorganic compounds. As a philosopher, he was a crusading materialist whose ideological views of race influenced later Nazi thought.

Huxley, Thomas Henry (1825–1895). A prolific British science writer and lecturer, Huxley served during the Victorian era as the chief public promoter of Darwin's theory of organic evolution. The son of a schoolteacher, Huxley attended medical school on scholarship. He secured a surgeon's post on a British navy ship and gained entry into British scientific circles on the basis of the natural history observations and collections that he sent back to England. Following his navy service, he taught at the School of Mines in London, held a series of prominent posts in British scientific organizations, and gained fame as a witty and irreverent public voice for science. When Darwin announced his theory of evolution in 1858, Huxley saw it as the ideal vehicle for promoting materialism in Western science and meritocracy in British society. His efforts in defending the theory of evolution in public debates and popular essays earned him the nickname "Darwin's bulldog." In later life, he became active in efforts to secularize the British educational system and coined the term "agnostic" to describe his own views on religion.

Lamarck, Chevalier de (1744–1829). Born the 11th son of a French nobleman and soldier, Lamarck's full name was Jean-Baptiste de Monet, Chevalier de Lamarck. After brief service in the French army, Lamarck devoted himself to the study of botany under royal patronage. After the French Revolution of 1789, Lamarck argued for the reorganization of biological studies on systematic, scientific grounds and was named curator of invertebrates at the National Museum of Natural History. Beginning in 1802, he published a series of works accounting for the evolution of new species through the inheritance of acquired characteristics. Although highly novel and widely known, Lamarck's theory did not gain a serious hearing by scientists until after Darwin published his alternative theory of evolution by natural selection in 1859. Thereafter, Lamarckism competed with Darwinism until Darwinism won out in the 20th century.

Leakey, Mary Douglas (1913–1996). British-born paleontologist who, with her husband, Louis Leakey, set the standard in the hunt for hominid fossils for half a century. Beginning in the 1920s, Louis Leakey established East Africa as the center for hominid fossil discovery. Mary Douglas joined Louis Leakey as a field researcher in 1935 and married him a year later. Together, they pioneered techniques of systematic excavation and meticulous documentation that raised standards in the field. In 1961, Mary Leakey shook the human family tree with her discovery of *Homo habilis*, the earliest known species in the genus *Homo*. First with her husband and later her son, Richard, Mary Leakey contributed to a series of other hominid fossil finds.

Lyell, Charles (1797–1875). A British gentleman-scientist, Lyell revolutionized the study of geology through his three-volume *Principles of Geology*, first published in the early 1830s. Giving up the practice of law to study geology, Lyell expounded the view earlier proposed by Scottish geologist Joseph Hutton that, given enough time, existing geologic forces (such as volcanoes, earthquakes, and erosion) were sufficient to shape all the earth's features. In doing so, he banished supernatural forces from geology and contributed to the increasingly naturalistic bent of British and American science. Lyell's evolutionary view of geologic history provided an intellectual foundation for Darwin's evolutionary view of biological history. Late in life and rich in scientific honors, Lyell became a critical early supporter of Darwin's theory of evolution.

Mendel, Gregor (1822–1884). An Austrian parochial school science teacher, Mendel discovered the laws of classical genetics. Mendel took an early interest in science and studied it at the University of Vienna in preparation for his planned career as a Catholic priest serving as a church schoolteacher. During the 1860s, in the course of his teaching at Brunn, Mendel conducted a series of breeding experiments with pea plants designed to test the inheritance of discontinuous traits. He found a regular pattern of dominant-recessive inheritance that became the basis for classical genetics. Mendel published his findings in a respected science journal, but their unexpected mathematical regularity led them to be ignored until 1900, by which time biological thinking had caught up with Mendel's experimental findings.

Morris, Henry M. (1918–). As a civil engineer during the 1940s, Morris developed an interest in the orderliness of nature. Already persuaded in the literal truth of the Bible, Morris became convinced that the Genesis accounts of a recent six-day creation and worldwide flood must be true. To study the matter further, he earned a doctorate degree in hydraulics from the University of Minnesota in 1950. For the next 25 years, Morris taught at state universities while writing a series of books on "flood geology," or his theory that Noah's flood could account for geologic features and the fossil record. He published the most influential of these books, *Genesis Flood*, with John C. Whitcomb, Jr., in 1961. It became highly popular in fundamentalist circles, reviving belief in a recent six-day creation and inspiring a political movement to secure balanced treatment for Morris's "scientific creationism" along with evolution in public schools. Since the late 1960s, Morris has led various Christian organizations that promote creation research and instruction.

Spencer, Herbert (1820–1903). One of the most controversial and influential English thinkers of the Victorian era, Spencer helped to lay the foundation for evolutionary thought in the social sciences. Beginning in the early 1850s, before Darwin announced the scientific theory of evolution by natural selection, Spencer published a series of influential sociological works attributing human progress to an evolutionary process driven by individualism. Change came through individual effort and could be inherited by the individual's offspring, Spencer maintained, in accord with his Lamarckian vision of evolution. In a bow to Darwinism, he added that competition then selected the fittest to survive and reproduce. Spencer advocated an extreme form of economic and social laissez faire, arguing that governmental and charitable welfare programs weakened society. Rejecting religion, he promoted a unification of all knowledge based on scientifically derived truths.

Wallace, Alfred Russel (1823–1913). A British naturalist and botanical collector, Wallace is best known for having independently deduced the theory of evolution by natural selection. From a working-class family, Wallace taught himself how to identify biological specimens at an early age. A radical thinker in religion and politics, Wallace accepted the idea of evolution as postulated by Lamarck and believed it could be proven by showing the geographic proximity of similar species. With the ulterior motive of studying bio-geography, Wallace set off as a commercial collector of exotic animals in the Amazon valley and Malay Archipelago from 1848 to 1862. In 1858, he conceived of natural selection as the mechanism driving evolution and sent an article outlining his idea to Charles Darwin. The receipt of this article moved Darwin to publish his own thoughts on the topic. Wallace's voluminous later writing centered on bio-geography, socialism, and spiritualism.

Wilson, Edward O. (1929–). Through his study of ants and other social insects, Wilson has shaped the frontiers of evolutionary biology over a 50-year-long career at Harvard University. As an enormously popular writer, he has effectively communicated these ideas to the public. At the center of his thinking is sociobiology, or the view that evolutionary biology (with its emphasis on individual survival and reproduction) provides a basis for understanding societal behavior patterns in animals. Extrapolating from social insects and other animals to humans, Wilson maintains that some human behaviors, such as aggression and sexuality, are conditioned by our evolutionary development. Even behaviors that appear altruistic can derive from instincts developed through natural selection, he argues, because such behavior on behalf of relatives preserves an individual's genetic representation in the next generation. For Wilson, sociobiology suggests an evolutionary basis for human ethics.

Bibliography

Essential Reading:

Bowler, Peter J. *Evolution: The History of an Idea*. Berkeley: University of California Press, 1984. The most accurate and up-to-date survey of the history of evolutionary thought; widely used in college courses on the history of science.

Darwin, Charles. *Voyage of the Beagle*, ed. Janet Browne and Michael Neve. London: Penguin Books, 1989. The standard edited version of Darwin's delightfully written 1839 journal of his 1831–1836 voyage aboard H.M.S. *Beagle*. This edition is widely used in college courses.

————. *On the Origin of Species*, intro. Ernst Mayr. Cambridge: Harvard University Press, 1964. The classic, highly readable first edition of Darwin's landmark argument for evolution by natural selection, here presented in a facsimile edition widely used as a college text.

————. "The Descent of Man," in Philip Appleman, ed., *Darwin*, 3rd ed. New York: W.W. Norton & Co., 2001, pp. 175–254. A selection of key chapters from Darwin's controversial treatise on human evolution.

Larson, Edward J. *Evolution's Workshop: God and Science on the Galapagos Islands*. New York: Basic Books, 2001. The lecturer's historical survey of scientific research on the Galapagos Islands, including analysis of the impact on evolutionary thought of the fieldwork conducted on the islands by Charles Darwin, Peter Lack, Peter and Rosemary Grant, and others.

————. *Summer for the Gods: The Scopes Trial and America's Continuing Debate Over Science and Religion*. Cambridge: Harvard University Press, 1998. The lecturer's Pulitzer Prize-winning account of the sensational 1925 trial of John Scopes for teaching evolution in violation of the Tennessee anti-evolution law.

Numbers, Ronald L. *The Creationists: The Evolution of Scientific Creationism*. Berkeley: University of California Press, 1993. The definitive history of the origins and influence of scientific creationism in conservative American Protestantism.

Supplementary Reading:

Allen, Garland. *Life Sciences in the Twentieth Century*. Cambridge: Cambridge University Press, 1978. A technical, textbook-like history of the biological sciences during the first half of the 20th century. It covers the rediscovery of Mendelian genetics and the emergence of the modern neo-Darwinian synthesis in evolutionary thought.

Behe, Michael J. *Darwin's Black Box: The Biochemical Challenge to Evolution*. New York: Simon & Schuster, 1996. Written for non-scientists, this book argues that biochemical molecules are too irreducibly complex to have evolved in a Darwinian fashion. This book is a foundational text for the Intelligent Design movement.

Bowler, Peter J. *The Non-Darwinian Revolution: Reinterpreting a Historical Myth*. Baltimore: Johns Hopkins University Press, 1988. A groundbreaking study of the history of evolutionary science during the late 19th century. As the author shows, evolution gained widespread acceptance even as Darwinism floundered.

Browne, Janet. *Charles Darwin: Voyaging*. Princeton: Princeton University Press, 1995. The first volume of the definitive two-volume biography of Charles Darwin. It covers the period from Darwin's birth through the mid-1850s.

Conkin, Paul K. *When All the Gods Trembled: Darwinism, Scopes, and American Intellectuals*. Lanham, MD: Rowman & Littlefield, 1998. A balanced, thoughtful analysis of the impact of evolutionary materialism on 20th-century American religious thought. The author is one of America's leading intellectual historians.

Dart, Raymond A. *Adventures with the Missing Link*. New York: Harper, 1959. A first-hand account of searching for and finding hominid fossils in South Africa.

Dawkins, Richard. *The Selfish Gene*. Oxford: Oxford University Press, 1976. A popular, readable account of the scientific view that the evolutionary dynamic operates at the gene level. A logical, utterly materialistic interpretation of modern Darwinian evolution.

Desmond, Adrian, and James Moore. *Darwin: The Life of a Tormented Evolutionist*. New York: Warner Books, 1992. An engaging one-volume biography of Charles Darwin that explores the religious, psychological, and intellectual impact on Darwin of his wrestling with evolution theory.

Edey, Maitland A., and Donald C. Johanson. *Blueprints: Solving the Mystery of Evolution*. Boston: Little, Brown & Co., 1989. A readable survey of the history of evolutionary science co-authored by a popular science writer and the discoverer of the fossil hominid Lucy. The book contains a lively description of hominid fossils.

Gould, Stephen Jay. *Wonderful Life: The Burgess Shale and the Nature of History*. New York: W.W. Norton, 1989. Perhaps the best of Gould's many popular and readable books about his punctuated equilibrium variant of Darwinian evolution. This book wonderfully presents evidence for evolution from geology and paleontology.

Greene, John C. *The Death of Adam: Evolution and Its Impact on Western Thought*. Ames: Iowa State University Press, 1959. The classic intellectual history of Darwin's theory of evolution by natural selection; widely used in college courses for generations. It focuses on intellectual currents leading up to Darwinism, with less emphasis on the intellectual impact of Darwinism.

Hofstadter, Richard. *Social Darwinism in American Thought*. Philadelphia: University of Pennsylvania Press, 1944. A highly critical history of laissez-faire economic and social doctrines in the United States written by a master historian shortly after such doctrines went out of vogue.

Johnson, Phillip E. *Darwin on Trial*. Downers Grove, IL: Intervarsity Press, 1993. The case against the scientific theory of evolution argued by a University of California law professor. This book gained wide popularity in evangelical Christian circles during the 1990s.

Kevles, Daniel J. *In the Name of Eugenics: Genetics and the Uses of Human Heredity*. New York: Knopf, 1985. An intellectual history of the Anglo-American eugenics movement written by America's premier historian of science.

Lack, David. *Darwin's Finches*. Cambridge: Cambridge University Press, 1947. The classic study of evolution among finches on the Galapagos Islands, this book offered key field evidence for the neo-Darwinian synthesis.

Larson, Edward J. *Sex, Race and Science: Eugenics in the Deep South*. Baltimore: Johns Hopkins University Press, 1995. The lecturer's study of eugenics practices in the American South. It includes background information on eugenics generally, which offers a concise introduction to the topic.

————. *Trial and Error: The American Controversy Over Creation and Evolution*, 2nd rev. ed. New York: Oxford University Press, 2002. The lecturer's historical survey of the controversy over the teaching of evolution in American public schools.

Livingstone, David N. *Darwin's Forgotten Defenders: The Encounter between Evangelical Theology and Evolutionary Thought.* Grand Rapids, MI: William B. Eerdmans, 1987. A historical study of conservative Protestant biologists in late 19th -century America who attempted to reconcile evolutionary science with Christian beliefs.

Lloyd, G. E. R. *Early Greek Science: Thales to Aristotle*. New York: W.W. Norton & Co., 1970. A classic survey of ancient Greek science; widely used as a college text.

Marsden, George M. *Understanding Fundamentalism and Evangelicalism.* Grand Rapids, MI: William B. Eerdmans, 1991. A historical comparison of two strains of conservative Protestant thought in the United States with a thoughtful discussion of their views on evolution and scientific creationism.

Mendel, Gregor Johann. *Experiments on Plant Hybridization*, intro. Paul C. Mangelsdorf. Cambridge: Harvard University Press, 1965. A reprint with introduction of Mendel's original scientific articles on genetics.

Numbers, Ronald L. *Darwinism Comes to America*. Cambridge: Harvard University Press, 1998. A historical overview designed for use in college courses of various scientific and religious responses to the introduction of evolutionary science in the United States.

Paul, Diane B. *Controlling Human Heredity: 1865 to the Present.* Atlantic Highlands, NJ: Humanities Press, 1995. A brief basic overview of the history of eugenics written as a supplementary text for college courses—clear and readable.

Raby, Peter. *Alfred Russel Wallace: A Life.* A readable new biography of Alfred Russel Wallace that places his complex scientific and religious views in context.

Shipman, Pat. *Man Who Found the Missing Link: Eugene Dubois's Thirty-Year Struggle to Prove Darwin Right.* New York: Simon & Schuster, 2001. A science journalist's highly readable biography of Eugene Dubois, who was the first person to discover hominid fossils.

Toumey, Christopher P. *God's Own Scientists: Creationists in a Secular World.* New Brunswick, NJ: Rutgers University Press, 1994. A sociologist's study of the conservative Christians who actively espouse scientific creationism and oppose secular humanism.

Wallace, Alfred Russel. "On the Tendency of Varieties to Depart Indefinitely from the Original Type," in Jane R. Camerini, ed., *The Alfred Russel Wallace Reader: A Selection of Writings from the Field.* Baltimore: Johns Hopkins University Press, 2001. Wallace's engaging original 1858 essay outlining his theory of evolution by natural selection.

————. "Spiritualism and Human Evolution," in Jane R. Camerini, ed., *The Alfred Russel Wallace Reader: A Selection of Writings from the Field.* Baltimore: Johns Hopkins University Press, 2001. A representative late essay by Wallace defending the limits of evolution as applied to human development.

Weiner, Jonathan. *The Beak of the Finch: A Story of Evolution in Our Time.* New York: Vintage Books, 1995. A science journalist's lively, well-written account of influential field research on Darwin's finches conducted by Peter and Rosemary Grant during the late 20th century.

Whitcomb, John C., and Henry M. Morris. *The Genesis Flood.* Nutley, NJ: Presbyterian and Reformed Publishing Co., 1961. The foundational text of scientific creationism containing arguments against evolution and for the scientific accuracy of the Genesis account of creation.